To Work Is Human

To Work Is Human
Mental Health and the
Business Community

Edited by ALAN MCLEAN, M.D.

*In cooperation with the National Association
of Manufacturers and the Center
for Occupational Mental Health
Cornell University Medical College*

The Macmillan Company, New York
Collier-Macmillan Limited, London

Library of Congress Catalog Card Number: 67-26640

First Printing

The Macmillan Company, New York
Collier-Macmillan Canada Ltd., Toronto, Ontario
Printed in the United States of America

Contents

Contents

Preface

Readers of a new book have more than a passing curiosity about its origin. I should like to satisfy that curiosity about this volume in a brief preface. *To Work Is Human: Mental Health and the Business Community* began when Douglas Caddy, then a program executive for the National Association of Manufacturers, and Robert Lounsbury, vice president-general counsel of the Eltra Corporation, then chairman of the Subcommittee on Mental Health of the NAM Employee Health and Safety Committee and president of the Center for Occupational Mental Health, first discussed the possibility of presenting to NAM's membership information on this subject of growing interest.

More than ever in past years, employee benefit programs do not differentiate between mental and physical illness. Costs to employers are rising as they cover treatment for psychiatric disorders. Workmen's Compensation benefits are frequently awarded to employees when mental disorders are found to be "caused" by the job. An increasing sense of social responsibility and sophistication in many companies extends to concern for employee disability, the support of community treatment facilities, and rehabilitation programs. There is also a vague awareness that mental health is probably related to productivity; that it therefore makes good economic sense for an employer to stimulate healthy behavior on the job.

As a result of their discussions, Mr. Caddy contacted me in my role as program director for the Center for Occupational Mental Health to explore the feasibility of a national conference on these subjects.

For some years the Center, with a small, part-time, professional, technical, and clerical staff had served as a nonprofit, independent agency providing information about occupational mental health to the National Clearinghouse for Mental Health Information of the National Institute of Mental Health. It continues to do so today as part of the Department of Psychiatry of Cornell University Medical College and is the only agency in the world concerned solely with occupational mental health.*

On March 17, 1966, the National Association of Manufacturers sponsored an exploratory, one-day meeting of the Board of Directors (now the Advisory Board) of the Center. The purpose was to review the possibility of a national conference and to see if there was an acceptable role for the Center in such an undertaking. In a free-wheeling discussion, the group expressed an initial consensus of reluctance to become involved with an employer's association, thereby perhaps jeopardizing its previously neutral position of concern for the employee. There was concern that the NAM, as a spokesman for manufacturers, might have ulterior motives. The somewhat more liberal leanings of the Center's directors emerged to test the expressed sincerity of NAM in undertak-

---

* Center staff members review more than one hundred professional journals each month as well as books, monographs, newspapers, and newsletters that may contain information in its field of interest. Significant documents are abstracted and coded for entry into the Clearinghouse information system and distributed to about seven thousand professional and business readers. In addition, *Occupational Mental Health Notes,* a regular publication of the Clearinghouse, is prepared at the Center. Bibliographies and review articles have also been published.

ing sponsorship of a program with avowed concern primarily for the individual worker.

These challenges were met and handled adroitly by NAM's then vice president of Industrial Relations, Charles Stenicka, and by Mr. Caddy. It was agreed that any venture would give to Center directors control of program content including selection of speakers and their topics. Sensing the conviction of NAM that service to its members was its principal motivation, those attending that exploratory meeting proceeded to sketch the format of the subsequent national conference.

This was done with the understanding that the final conference should not be another one-day, flash-in-the-pan reiteration of mental health sermonizing. Further, a one-day conference, properly prepared, should not be an end in itself. It should adequately represent a selection of current data available for application within the business community. It should reflect present-day research from the clinical and behavioral sciences, as well as from related disciplines. It should say something of current thinking in psychiatry, occupational medicine, and the social sciences, as well as from the federal government and voluntary mental health agencies.

A series of technical conferences to determine the research needs in various aspects of the field was also being considered by the Center directors at that time. These conferences were to produce another volume to spell out the recommendations of more than one hundred experts for future studies to develop new areas of understanding of employee mental health.

A companion volume summarizing current application of previous research and program activities for the "consumer" —the employer—seemed an appropriate undertaking. A reasonable vehicle for developing such a book could well be the conference cosponsored with NAM. Speakers would have to be carefully selected and agree to prepare material not just for the listening audience but for publication as well. They would have to further agree to a careful interchange of information in advance of the meeting to prevent overlap and to stimulate crossfertilization of ideas. They would further need to represent unions, management, and the professions while still integrating their material, one with another.

They all did so.

Obviously we could not include a sample of all the points of view in occupational mental health. Our primary goal was representational, leaving for later volumes the development of many of the themes outlined here. From the behavioral sciences, in particular, greater elaboration would have rounded out the picture. A better balance might have been achieved with additional material on job satisfaction, testing, achievement, survey techniques, and motivation. From both the clinical and behavioral sciences, it would have been useful to include more material on management and medical education. Such are the problems inherent in any time frame.

As it is, this book provides a contemporary introduction, largely in consumer terms, of much that is known in our subject field. This volume contains the joint efforts of nineteen people well qualified to speak on their subjects. Each took time from a busy schedule to work with me on this book. It is with warm thanks that I acknowledge their willingness to develop and exchange ideas and outlines and to prepare final manuscripts, all in advance of the National Conference on Mental Health and the Business Community held in New York City on October 21, 1966.

Particular thanks are due Dr. Richard A. Dunnington, manager of Personnel Research for the IBM Company and a director of the Center, who worked closely with me throughout the planning of this project, the Center staff including my assistant Mrs. Hannah Wedeen, and my secretary Miss Hilda Wartholowitz, who patiently participated in each phase of the preparation of this book. For the title we are indebted to Mrs. Hermine Popper.

Appreciation should also be expressed to members of the NAM staff who were actively involved in the conference itself, in addition to Mr. Caddy. They included William K. Zinke, who succeeded Mr. Stenicka as vice president of Industrial Relations, and Mrs. Phyllis H. Moehrle, assistant to the vice president of Industrial Relations.

ALAN McLEAN

White Plains, New York
Fall 1967

I

The Challenge

1 Introduction: Industry on the Couch?

Alan McLean

Mental health is an illusive commodity; a highly personal matter. It is bound to our private thoughts and feelings and concerned with our behavior. It helps determine our beliefs and our perceptions. That we all occasionally retreat into symptoms, be they psychosomatic reactions in our bowels or feelings of depression or withdrawal from the real world, is entirely our own concern.

Or is it?

Why should these personal reactions be of concern to our employers? Why should a boss be concerned? Isn't there enough of Big Brother in this world without the sophisticated involvement of psychiatrists, psychologists, and industrial physicians employed by a company?

And what is mental health anyway? How does it relate to the work we do? Does it relate to productivity, to job satisfaction? Is it possible for an employer to be other than economically selfish in his concern for the mental health of those in his employ?

3

For that matter, why should the National Institute of Mental Health—the chief federal agency concerned with mental illness and mental health—designate occupational mental health as one of its major fields of interest? And why should an employers' association be interested in sponsoring a national conference on the subject?

Since the 1920's, many capable, ethical, and objective professionals have been concerned with the mental health and mental illness of people at work. They have studied the process of vocational rehabilitation of those who have suffered incapacitating psychiatric disorder. They have researched those aspects of the work environment that both promote and impede mentally healthy behavior. Confidential psychiatric and psychological services have been provided to employees while at work to assist them in coping with symptoms of emotional reactions. Consultation has been provided the management of many companies by capable professionals to help them understand the on-the-job behavior of employees with emotional disturbances. Techniques have been developed and used by such professionals to reduce the unhealthy stress inherent in some jobs. The research of behavioral scientists is becoming less basic and more applied as it too suggests measures to prevent adverse emotional reactions on the job.

Meanwhile, a variety of influences stimulate increasing interest on the part of the employing organization. Workmen's compensation boards have held that mental illness incurred as a result of job stress is compensable. At the bargaining table unions are winning benefits to provide psychiatric treatment for their employees and their families. The crippling of a valuable employee by a psychiatric disorder is costly to both the company and the community. Arbitrators are insisting that corporate responsibility extends to include the taking of reasonable steps to insure against a stressful work environment and to a responsibility for preventive measures. The President's Committee on the Employment of the Handicapped no longer includes the word "physically" in its title. Paralleling these national developments, those in the professions are increasingly active. While relatively few in number, psychiatrists are being trained to think in terms of preventive and community psychiatry including the world of work. In the past, Cornell University and more recently the Menninger Foundation have offered intensive training for the psychiatrist interested in becoming an industrial consultant. The American Psychiatric Association, the Group for the Advancement of Psychiatry, the Industrial Medical Association, and the American Medical Association —spokesmen for their specialties—have committees or councils concerned with industrial mental health. In the past decade, the Menninger Foundation alone has taught more than 1,000 top executives in intensive one-week courses on mental health principles. They have provided similar courses for 400 industrial physicians.

In a one-page feature, "Mental Health on the Job: Industry's $3-billion Problem," *Time*, in May of 1960, said that many businessmen are coming to believe that it is only "practical humanitarianism" to try to increase efficiency by improving employees' mental health. To both doctors and executives the problem of mental health is finally out in the open where it can be defined, understood, and discussed. Out of the discussion over how to handle the problem, industry is sure to gain new awareness of the need for mental health among its workers and, gradually, to do more and more about it.

Many of the major business publications have carried articles on this subject. The *Wall Street Journal* has run front-page stories on psychiatric programs in industry. *Business Week, Business Management,* and the *Harvard Business Re-*

view are but a few of the periodicals addressed to the businessman that have pursued this subject in varying depth and frequency. Trade magazines for subspecialty groups in industry have also featured stories. They include *Iron Age, Employee Relations Bulletin, Industrial Relations News, NAM Reports, Factory Management,* and *Women's Wear Daily.* There should be little surprise that the focus of interest has attained a sufficient level to insure the success of a national conference sponsored by a business organization.

With mounting employer and professional concern, how is it possible to enhance the mental health of an employee population and prevent the development of psychiatric disorder —both without infringing upon the ethical, moral, and highly proprietary rights of the individual? How can one prevent "deep therapy on the assembly line" while encouraging mentally healthy behavior in employees? How can the responsible employer assist in the rehabilitation of those who have had a disabling psychiatric disorder? The answers to these questions are addressed by the authors in the following chapters. To establish a frame of reference let us first examine the concept: mental health.

WHAT IS MENTAL HEALTH?[1]

We are really considering two distinct concepts throughout this volume. One is mental health, and the other is mental illness. They are not *necessarily* related. At this point, it would be wise, I think, to define our terms—distinguish between the concepts and briefly discuss each separately.

First, the pleasanter but more diffuse question of mental health. Here is a phrase that has replaced the more tradi-

---

[1] This section is freely adapted from an article by the author, "Who Pays the Bill? A Clinical Perspective," appearing in the May 1967 issue of the *Journal of Occupational Medicine.*

tional "mental hygiene" and that seems at times synonymous with the phrase "human relations." There seems to be implicit in several chapters in this volume a feeling that an employer's responsibility is to provide meaning, satisfaction, and stimulation, but no stress or anxiety, in the work situation for his employees. Regardless of one's definition of mental health, no employer is really able to assume such a contractual commitment. It is an impossibility even for a company that has, high on its list of corporate values, a belief that every worker should be placed in a job situation properly suited to his skills and interests. Products and processes are ever changing. Industrial growth means change, and change disrupts the comfortable and satisfying routine of many jobs. Out of change itself come feelings of tension and anxiety. Out of some tension and some anxiety comes the stimulus for personal growth—the motivation of broadening levels of skill and ability. Industry must change to survive. Its fundamental role in life is not the fostering of mental health, but the creation of marketable products and services in a competitive world.

Let us examine one concept of mental health, however, and briefly review elements that can support healthy behavior at work.

The mental health of any single individual is the product of a unique, overwhelmingly complex personality interacting continuously with a total life situation. By the time someone comes into the work force, his personality is well formed. His ability to cope with future life situations in a healthy way, or a less healthy one, has already been largely determined.

The work of Solley and Munden[2] produced a definition that says the individual who is mentally healthy is one who

[2] C.M. Solley and K.J. Munden, "Behavior of The Mentally Healthy," *Bulletin of The Menninger Clinic* 26 (1962): 178-188.

has a wide variety of sources of gratification. While he does not have his irons in every fire, his pleasures come in different ways and from many things. He is an individual who is flexible in situations that are stressful for him. He rolls with the punch. When faced with problems, he can see alternate solutions. He treats others as individuals. He recognizes that they have different value systems, and he does not attempt to inflict his own beliefs upon them. He is not tied up completely within himself. On the other hand, he has a fairly good understanding and, more important, an acceptance of his own limitations and his own assets. For this reason, he sets his goals realistically and rarely bites off more than he can chew. Finally, such a person is one who is active and productive—appropriately and realistically participating in the world around him.

I suppose this could be thought of as a definition of an ideal personality. We can certainly equate mental health with such an ideal. It is also a definition of healthy behavior. While few employers have an overriding sense of obligation to stimulate healthy behavior among their employees, many would acknowledge that it would be pleasant, indeed, if their work force could be made up of people who at least approached the characteristics in this definition. And while one cannot alter basic personality, an employer *can* encourage such behavior.

A constricted, monotonous, and limited job can be made to provide additional sources of satisfaction by a thoughtful management. Through job enlargement, the encouragement of interests and participation beyond the narrow task at hand, the individual worker can be led to broaden his horizons. Additional sources of gratification can come in appropriate rewards from supervision.

The definition suggests allowing flexibility of individual reactions and behavior. If one defines narrow patterns of expected behavior and spells out rules for each possible action, an organization will probably get just what it asks for. No more, no less. Treating an employee as a child provokes childlike behavior. Allowing an individual freedom of expression and judgment tends to provoke more mature, responsible, and adult behavior, the stimulation of innovation and involvement with the ultimate advantage accruing to both the individual and the organization.

If realistically handled, a job allows an individual to test his own beliefs about himself and his skills and abilities as well as his inadequacies. Through various job appraisal systems, he has an opportunity to validate his own beliefs about his productive skills. Properly handled, these techniques can be harnessed to provide continuing feedback to the worker. Whether it be through wage increases based on performance, upon promotion or assignment to more interesting jobs, reinforcement of perceptions of one's strengths and weaknesses becomes both a prop to mental health and a useful motivating force for the employer.

The stimulation of mental health may be far from the minds of most employers. It may be an elusive Utopian goal. No research study has yet proved a direct correlation with productivity. But there seems to be ample evidence that the mutual goals of industrial efficiency and productivity share a set of common concepts based on respect for the individual.

Mental illness also has its roots in the same equation of an individual personality interacting with its total life situation. But such disorders are specific diagnostic entities. They are carefully and officially defined in the Diagnostic and Statistical Manual for Mental Disorders published by the American Psychiatric Association and included in the Standard Nomenclature of Diseases and Operations approved by the American Medical Association. They are determined by

9

careful psychiatric and psychological evaluation of a single patient.

One could argue convincingly that industry should not be singled out for a particular responsibility for the mental disorders of its employees. After all, the employer receives an end-product—an extraordinarily complex personality, well-formed and difficult to fully assess. The potential for development of a mental disorder comes with each worker in varying degree. The identical work situation that may trigger an overwhelming psychotic reaction in one employee may be the very situation which proves a stimulus to mental health in another. Should industry be held accountable for the provision of a stress-free environment when each individual's vulnerability is so unique? I am not convinced that such accountability is either fair or reasonable!

There is, however, a definite trend toward *some* acceptance by employers and by unions of reasonable responsibility for providing treatment for mental disorders of employees and members of their families. In-company medical programs of a great many larger employers are increasingly concerned with such illnesses. The occupational physician responsible for such programs is becoming much more sophisticated in the diagnosis and the management of these disorders. The doctor in industry is now concerned with early detection of such illness, recognizing as he does that most such disorders are far more amenable to treatment at their onset. He is concerned with appropriate referral of employee-patients for evaluation and with treatment by a private physician or a community agency. He also has a goal of work assignments that considers the employees' psychiatric status. No physician in or out of industry wants to see his patient placed in a work situation that would make a known mental disorder worse.

Through increasing support of in-company medical programs, the management of our larger and more sophisticated companies express an appropriate responsibility for both physical and mental health at work. I do not suggest that all industrial medical programs are sophisticated or that all large employers have assumed a like responsibility for employee health. I speak of a trend.

It is the furtherance of this trend we hope to encourage.

2   The Age of
Industrial Sophistication

W. P. Gullander

In an age of increasing industrial sophistication, the use of skills, concepts, and techniques from the clinical and the behavioral sciences will be increasingly important to a management concerned with the effective utilization of people. The relationship between morale, productivity, job satisfaction, and mental health in a working population is increasingly clear. In this chapter, I asked Mr. Gullander to set the stage and to suggest reasons for the concern of the business manager in the mental health of his employees. Why is the National Association of Manufacturers sufficiently interested in this topic to cosponsor a national conference? What related activities is the NAM engaged in?

Mr. Gullander has had an illustrious business career, climaxed in 1962 with his election as chief executive officer of NAM. He has applied proven business principles to the operations of the seventy-year-old association and brought a managerial flair for problem-solving to this national group. Previously he was executive vice president and a director of General Dynamics Corporation and before that a vice president of the Weyerhaeuser Company. At the outset of his business career, he served for twenty-two years with the General Electric Company. He is a member of the National Export Expansion Council of the United States Department of Commerce; Citizens Committee on Business and Industry; National Citizens Commission on International Co-operation; National Citizens Committee for Community Relations; National Institute of Social Sciences; Task Force on Youth Employment Opportunities; Aspen Society of Fellows; and member at large of the National Council, Boy Scouts of America. A graduate of the University of Minnesota, Mr. Gullander also holds an honorary Doctor of Laws degree from the University of Puget Sound.

In one sense, Mr. Gullander is an old hand at assisting in the treatment of psychiatric disorder. During his college years, he supported himself by serving as a full-time companion to a young man with a schizophrenic reaction. This experience, with its trying times and minor victories, gave him an early and meaningful exposure to the problems and promises of mental illness described in this volume.

The National Association of Manufacturers regards this book and the conference on which it was based as landmark events. The conference represented a "first" in many ways. Never before had industry sponsored a meeting on mental health at the national level. No other management organization, to our knowledge, had called such a session exclusively to consider mental health in its relation to the business community.

Recognizing that, because of their complexity, problems of this nature require the best thinking of the entire community, we opened the doors to make it a public conference. We were happy so many people from the professions, labor, government, and the public joined us to focus on the subject of mental health and to explore ways and means for dealing with stress situations as they affect employees.

That NAM should be the vehicle for convening such a conference is, I hope, as gratifying a sign to you as it is to me. It illustrates the leadership role that NAM can play as the spokesman for industry. As I see it, the sponsorship of the conference by some forty of the nation's leading industrialists, under NAM's auspices, is powerful evidence that (1) manufacturers recognize the growing number of plant situations that call for greater understanding of the employee's emotional needs; (2) management is increasingly sensitive to its social responsibilities; and (3) we are cognizant of the contribution that every group represented at the meeting can make; each has a stake in finding solutions to mental health problems.

THE AGE OF INDUSTRIAL SOPHISTICATION—WHAT IT MEANS

The phrase "age of industrial sophistication" flashes a whole set of specific meanings. Human experience and history use this term to indicate a recognizable period, marked by certain distinctives, but a period in transition, a way station.

In this age of industrial sophistication we, too, are moving from a dynamic past to an exciting future. And this age reflects the pivotal role of industry as a leader and as an innovator in the development and utilization of both our technological and human resources.

Sophistication, Webster tells us, is to be highly complicated, deprived of original simplicity, complex, finely experienced, and aware. This is our age.

EMERGING PLANT ENVIRONMENT

The products that are on industry's drawing boards and in our laboratories are incredibly sophisticated and becoming more so. We will soon be traveling in giant jets that fly 1800 miles per hour, carrying 350 of us at once in supersonic transports. We will be eating synthetic foods that taste exactly like the real thing. We will be growing wall-to-wall carpeting by scattering a chemical substance on our living room floors.

We are building machines that can perform functions far beyond our wildest dreams, but it is popular today to decry this progress, to view it with alarm, and to picture it as man's enemy.

The more we learn about it, the more we recognize that automation and technology cannot replace—indeed they magnify and make more urgent—the need for intelligent human judgments. It is man and man alone who must give technology its values, applying it with wisdom and purpose.

In transforming America from a society of scarcity to one of abundance, profound changes have taken place in the kinds of jobs available to Americans. Thousands of jobs are disappearing and more thousands of jobs are being created. New Industries are being born almost daily and old ones are declining; consumer demand is shifting, and so are the needs of heavy industry.

The essence of our times has made two kinds of demands on our people due to the changing nature and location of work. Jobs are calling for new skills and the willingness to learn them and adapt. The shifting fortunes of companies, new inventions, and new information cause operations to phase out here and spring up there, requiring employees to change jobs.

As part of the emerging pattern, it is realistic to expect that it will be the norm for some Americans to have three or four different careers in their lifetimes, perhaps requiring them to move with their families to a number of different localities. There may be a resulting sense of rootlessness and superficial relationships to others in the community when one doesn't expect to stay very long.

But change is itself essential to progress and it is always present in the work place. Contrary to popular impression, situations causing employee displacement are by no means limited to automation and new technology. Built into the industrial process itself is the search for better methods and the improvements that mean change. When this process is working properly, it inevitably results in people moving from one job to another. Old jobs are disappearing, and new jobs are constantly being created. The rapidity with which these changes are taking place brings a further burden to bear. A prodigious knowledge explosion is the mark of our times. We know four times as much as we knew in 1935—and in the next fifteen years scientists will learn as much as in all previous history! More scientific papers have been published since 1950 than in all the years preceding!

Scientific and technical information is doubling every year, causing an enormous log jam of new ideas. When this new knowledge is translated to plant operation, it means change and more change. The effects of rapid, frequent change are discomfiting to a man. Even small animals in the laboratory have difficulty adapting, and their elemental life is not complicated by the thousand crosscurrents affecting the actions and reactions of modern man.

To new technology and rapid change, I add three more factors as possibly producing mental strain for some people.

1. *New Patterns of Management.* As industrial corporations have grown in response to society's changing needs, they have found it necessary to make almost revolutionary changes in the techniques of managing.

In days to come, I see an avalanche of the untraditional. Our whole concept of managing is undergoing radical change, partly through necessity and partly through our growing knowledge of what it takes to secure effective operation.

Some of these changing patterns may be the cause of

stress, and we need to develop better ways of dealing with them.

For example, because of the shortage of executive talent, many companies today are hiring bright, young graduate school students and moving then into extremely responsible positions that formerly were the exclusive preserve of seasoned executives. Youth has no corner on flexibility, but willingness to try the impossible, to branch out into untried fields, often results in the recent graduate supervising experienced men who are two or three decades his senior. The resentments and conflicts that result are obvious.

Emotional disturbances are generated in many ways— status changes, promotion and demotion, shifts in program and assignment, arrival and departure of key personnel, styles of supervision, conflicting obligations, and the need to live with uncertainty.

Many traditional management concepts are dying. Our concepts of work and reward, loyalty and incentive are being reevaluated. Studies of tomorrow's management tell us that decision-making at all levels of management—from the frontline supervisor to the man at the top—are in for major revamping. The organization man is being relegated to limbo. More individual leeway, more responsibility for results, heavy accent on planning at the top, quicker action at middle levels—and new teamwork between men and machines, led by dynamic men who know how to build an organization where authority and freedom are wisely mixed —this is the new look.

2. *Growing Leisure Time.* One important way to neutralize on-the-job tensions is to make wiser use of our leisure time, and we're going to have more of it to use. Some leading economists hold the opinion that within the next thirty years, a normal week's schedule will be: work 20 hours, sleep 50–55 hours, free time nearly 100 hours.

But unwisely used, increased leisure can trigger problem

behavior, and this is a whole area that needs attention as we look toward more time off the job.

3. *Outside-the-Plant Factors.* Not all the challenging situations are on the job. Our whole socio-economic-political system is impacting the individual directly, assaulting him with complex and conflicting demands.

Even a surface examination of the conditions of the world today causes concern and sometimes fear in the hearts of all but the unthinking and callous. We are spread abroad with staggering commitments, both military and financial. We have fallen heir to world leadership with its towering moral requirements.

As individuals, we worry about newspaper headlines, about Vietnam, about more taxes and inflation. We have Dow-Jones jitters. We worry about the decline of public order, crime in the streets, and race riots. We worry about traffic jams and air pollution, about ferment on the campus, about poverty, narcotics, and school dropouts. We worry about our military supremacy—allegedly on the decline—a reawakening Red China, and the possibility of nuclear holocaust. No small wonder that as individuals, as well as a nation, we are unsettled by our turbulent times and some of us are unable to cope with life.

A well-established link is now assumed between psychological well-being on the one hand and social and economic well-being on the other, based in the long run on the capacities of individuals to work, live, and act in collective harmony. The relationship between an individual's mental health and his cultural environment is becoming more and more direct in our shrinking world.

All of the foregoing—the impact of new technology, of rapid and frequent change, of new patterns of management, growing leisure time, and the outside-the-plant factors of an affluent society in a turbulent world—make tremendous demands on the individual's ability to adjust.

There is no question that all of these elements confront the human spirit with cataclysmic force. This quiet revolution is "rattling our cage." Not a single person has not been affected profoundly by it. But some individuals—by heredity, environment, and personal faith—are better equipped to cope with the pressures of life in our times.

FOCUS ON THE EMPLOYEE

Industry is desirous of coming to grips with disturbed employee behavior. But in this age of industrial sophistication, we are committed to the positive frame of reference—the development of mental health. We are concerned with the effective utilization of people, not as tools of productivity, but because the employee whose job offers him opportunity for growth and a chance to relate to others in a meaningful way will find real fulfillment and satisfaction in his job. The clinical and behavioral sciences are developing skills, concepts, and techniques that are increasingly important to management in meeting the demands of this task.

Robert E. Chasen, president of Federal Electric Corporation, a subsidiary of International Telephone and Telegraph Corporation, put it well recently when he said, "Despite the knowledge explosion, despite the plethora of Ph.D. theses on employee relations, there are still millions of employees in the U.S. who get such little satisfaction from their daily jobs that they look forward to evenings and weekends for the opportunity to live and do something that gives them a real sense of satisfaction. . . . To what extent have we in management been responsible for this poor motivation? Do we really know the people who work for us? Have we lost the human touch? We need much more research and study on how to motivate human beings to higher levels of performance . . . on how to give every employee the opportunity to achieve real fulfillment on the job. For this age of change is an age that demands a sense of commitment and top performance not only from management but from every employee."

In the final analysis, the difference between the success and failure of a corporation lies in the way management treats its human resources, encouraging employees to make their maximum contribution by assuring that they are fitted to their tasks, by recognizing the importance of their work, by requiring supervisors to help employees in their jobs and to be genuinely interested in what they do, by permitting employees a maximum degree of initiative and self-expression.

Employee morale and motivational studies have shown that certain conditions, such as job security, type of work, and being a part of things, rank above salary. Material rewards are still important, but mostly if they are not provided. There is mounting evidence that industry needs to pay more attention to personal factors that slow down productivity, cause accidents, and undermine morale. We have a growing awareness that

1. the anxiety felt by the new employee slows down his adjustment to his work and postpones the time when he can be an effective performer;
2. emotional illness causes more absenteeism than any other illness except the common cold;
3. troubled people can interfere with the efficiency of any work group;
4. the three A's—Accidents, Absenteeism, and Alcoholism—are costing industry billions of dollars a year;
5. the man whose mind is diverted because of gnawing personal problems at home can make a mistake on his job that could be fatal to himself and to others, or could cause serious work disruption; and
6. mental disorders can be triggered by continuing super-

visory criticism without any effort to help an employee perform the job correctly.

Just the other day the Connecticut Board of Mediation and Arbitration ruled that discharge of a defiant worker was too harsh a penalty in view of management's failure to do something about the pent-up tensions in his department.

Employees and managers may be technically qualified for the job but nevertheless fail to produce effectively because of personal maladjustments. Further, some jobs in themselves tend to "trigger" problem behavior. This is why selection and placement take on new importance. If a man's personality is mismatched to a job, emotional upsets may ensue that could be costly in many ways. Some people can't take pressure; others can't take routine, meaningless tasks.

It isn't only machinery that breaks down. Employees, too, sometimes (and it seems in growing numbers) find themselves unable to adjust to a working environment where there is friction with fellow workers or with supervisors; where tensions are set up because of shifting or accelerating organizational demands, competition with younger people, conflicting loyalties, and frustrating interpersonal relations.

Machinery experts tell us that friction can destroy or damage a machine rapidly. We must remember that friction can also destroy or damage the sensitive human mechanism!

People in emotional trouble show it in many ways. We all know the belligerent employee who walks around with a chip on his shoulder, ready to argue at the slightest excuse; the man who gets "the blues" every other day, and often has the feeling that "nothing really matters"; the exaggerated worrier who is constantly anxious about minor details; the suspicious individual who is convinced others are out to get him; the selfish, greedy one who never thinks of the needs of others; the leaner who can't make decisions and lets others carry the load; the man who has poor emotional control, loses his temper, and engages in emotional outbursts out of all proportion to the problem.

In themselves these manifestations may not be serious, but they are warning flags—and if severe and prolonged, they could lead to mental illness.

Let me ask: What's the weather in your company? Is the outlook for fair and warmer—or are there some storm clouds ahead? To take a reading on the company's barometer, you need to do some simple calculations: What kind of gripes are you getting? Are employees' complaints taken seriously? Are they listened to? And most of all, do your people have an outlet they feel free to use—or do gripes get bottled up and grumbled about until they explode?

More sleep is lost because there is no safety valve, no way to sound off—and companies that don't give gripes a channel for bubbling to the surface lose out two ways. They are allowing a potentially dangerous situation to go uncorrected, and they are cutting themselves off from valuable feedback that could point the way to improvements in morale and productivity. For criticism can be a blessing in disguise—it can become the springboard for better performance and higher morale.

Summing up, research studies at Yale University underline management's responsibility to administer a complex social system. Within that system the supervisor-employee relationship is crucial, for that is where management's objectives intersect with employee attitudes. Management's job is, therefore, to achieve (1) effective utilization of the human resources available in carrying out the organization's goals and objectives, and (2) satisfaction of the human and social needs of members of the organization.

The fact is that despite all our sophistication, we still have a lot to learn about how to perform the management functions well. That's another reason why the nation's top experts in all phases of this complex field of mental health have contributed to this book.

Speaking for NAM, we welcome the opportunity to help lead the way toward stimulating greater attention in industry to the importance of mental health.

If management is to perform its proper function, it must be aware of and responsive to the social needs of employees. It is important that industry show the same resourcefulness and ingenuity in social dynamics that have been shown in production and in marketing.

We hope that from this volume will come a new dedication to finding solutions that will redound to the benefit of employee, employer and society as a whole: alleviation of mental or emotional stress for the individual; greater job satisfaction; greater commitment to company goals and objectives; greater efficiency and lower costs; increased productivity; and more profitable operation. These will be some of the values in the plant which can improve the industrial climate and our national life as well.

CONCLUSION

The world suffered an irreparable loss when Dr. William C. Menninger recently succumbed to a malignancy. I knew him well. As an outspoken advocate of mental health treatment, he helped enormously to break down the idea that psychiatry was either hilariously funny or sacrilegious or maybe even subversive.

Dr. Will, like Freud, believed that most personality disorders were caused by conscious or unconscious conflicts between selfish desires and what society demanded. He had this simple illustration of conscious versus unconscious conflict. The mind is something like two clowns cavorting in a horse's costume. The man up front (the conscious part) tries to determine the direction and make the whole animal behave. But he can never be sure what the man at the rear (the unconscious part) is going to do next. If both ends of the horse are going in the same direction, the individual's mental health is all right. If they are not pulling together, there is likely to be trouble.

The purpose of this Conference was to stimulate more people in pulling together on an important subject. It is our hope that, in doing so, some giant strides will be made in improving mental health in America.

3 The Challenge
to American Industry

Robert B. O'Connor

It would be difficult to find a man better suited to discuss the problems of mental disorder facing American industry than Robert B. O'Connor. He is an industrial vice president in charge of health services for the United States Steel Corporation. In this capacity, his responsibilities include not only the medical department but also personnel research, safety, and emergency planning. He is a respected physician who received his medical degree from Harvard Medical School in 1939 and is certified as a specialist in occupational medicine by the American Board of Preventive Medicine. In the finest traditions of the medical sciences, he has taught at the Harvard School of Public Health and at Tufts Medical School. Presently he is adjunct professor of occupational medicine, University of Pittsburgh School of Public Health. More important for his colleagues in occupational medicine, he is editor in chief of Journal of Occupational Medicine, *one of the three leading journals in his specialty.*

For one who started his career with several years training in surgery, it is perhaps unique to find Dr. O'Connor particularly concerned with people and their emotional problems. Yet it was Dr. O'Connor who, as medical director of U.S. Steel, founded its psychiatric program. Indeed, soon after his promotion to vice president he appointed his psychiatric consultant director of Psychiatric Services with status coequal to the medical director. He is a member of the Medical Advisory Board of the President's Committee on Employment of the Handicapped and of the Council on Voluntary Health Agencies of the American Medical Association.

I asked Dr. O'Connor to define the nature of occupational mental health problems in the work setting. I suggested that he might want to think about these questions as he prepared this chapter: What percentage of employees in the work force present or may develop psychopathology that interferes with effective work performance? What manifestations of these symptoms may be apparent to an employer? What specific challenges face those in the medical department, the personnel department, personnel research staff members or line managers?

In partial answer Dr. O'Connor notes that the occurrence of emotional problems of greater or lesser severity approaches 100 percent in a long enough time span. He goes on to say that, as a corollary of this, there will be employees who have all degrees of emotional stability. "There will be some who have been wobbling along through life on such an uneven keel that most of their energy is used up to keep their own boat bailed out with little energy left over for working and living." It is with such a frame of reference that Dr. O'Connor writes of the challenge of mental health problems to American industry.

A major challenge to American industry stems from the fact that human beings persist in acting like human beings.

Industrial management is comfortable with measurable, predictable things. Machines, materials, money, and manufacturing operations are *not* uncomplicated but they *are* susceptible to measurement, and to a considerable degree causes and effects are predictable. But human beings appear to be human enigmas. Even the most astute executive, with a high degree of intuitive understanding of people, wishes he could measure and manage the people part of his business as confidently as the material part.

This is true in the supervisor's day-to-day relationships with his subordinates. It becomes blatantly and confusingly true if an emotional problem or mental illness is involved. And so, although our primary concern is mental health, a significant part of this volume will be devoted to mental illness.

Mental illness is not an ideal term because it is too apt to connote major mental aberrations, such as schizophrenic and manic depressive reactions. Industry is concerned with the whole range of human behavior and so a more widely inclusive term, perhaps "emotional problems," would be more useful for us.

Although the problem case presents the more immediate and obvious need, mental health should be the more fruitful long-term goal.

Whatever the terms, we will at the outset be talking about people who have some degree of disablement in one or more of the functions of living. From the famous Manhattan study[1], we know that the incidence of emotional problems is high, probably as high as one in four in the general population. One would expect that it would be considerably lower in the industrial population, because there is selection at the time of employment and continuing further selection because of continuing at work. There are no equivalent studies of the industrial population, but a good estimate might be one in eight or ten. However, all of us are likely at one time or another to have an emotional problem of a greater or

---

[1] L. Srole, T.S. Langer, S.T. Michael, M.K. Opler, and T.A.C. Rennie, *Mental Health in the Metropolis: The Midtown Manhattan Study* (New York: McGraw-Hill, 1962).

lesser degree of seriousness. And so, while mental illness is surprisingly ubiquitous, the incidence of emotional problems in any group, over a long enough time span, will approach 100 percent.

Most of the major industries today have industrial medical programs of one sort or another. To a significant degree their focus is on organic medical illness. Yet a case of emotional illness can have a far more pervasive and disruptive effect on the functioning of a department. It can be far more subtle and difficult to identify, evaluate, and treat.

Subtle, pervasive, and disruptive are useful adjectives to describe the characteristics of a majority of emotional problem cases in industry; subtle because the behavior of the individual is often not blatantly abnormal; pervasive because it can involve a unit or section for a considerable period of time before being properly identified; and disruptive because it so often distorts interpersonal relationships, and such relationships are at the core of effective functioning of a unit.

Identification is not *always* difficult. I once saw a man in industry at the request of his supervisor because the man was found to be regularly using an unconnected telephone that hung on the wall near his machine. Before making any decision, he would use that phone to talk with and obtain advice from three sources. They were Bing Crosby, Harry Truman, and God—in that order. Without impugning the consultative qualifications of these three sources, one can say with a fair degree of confidence that this was not normal behavior.

On the other hand, paranoid ideas (delusions of persecution) may be described with seeming clarity and logic by an individual who appears to be quite intact.

There are numerous clues to the identification of an emotional problem, such as manner, demeanor, interpersonal relations, deterioration of work performance, and the like. But in many instances, there are no obvious clues. The individual may be bottling up within himself and masking from the rest of the world a painful anxiety or depression. And it must be accepted, too, that some of these are transient or self-limited, or are resolved more or less successfully by the individual without intrusion or intervention by others.

Once the case is identified, the next step is evaluation, parallel in many ways to determining diagnosis and prognosis in organic medicine. Evaluation in industry is often provided by the industrial physician—with greater or lesser degrees of expertise. Answers are needed to questions such as these: Is the patient dangerous to himself or others? Can he be safely kept at work? Does he have a true psychosis? Would he benefit by referral to an outside psychiatrist? Expert appraisal, that provides more competent answers to questions such as these, is *one* of the important reasons for having an industrial psychiatrist in the company medical department.

From such appraisal the next step—disposition of the problem case—is derived. Without it, disposition is apt to be fumbling; and fumbling is all too common.

This brings us to the other side of the coin—the matter of mental health. The great contribution of Freud was to provide information about, and to focus attention on, the molding effect of the multitude of things that surround the evolving personality of infancy and childhood. There is growing awareness, however, that this is but part of one of the four major cause and effect relationships in mental health. In addition to psychological, there are also biological, societal, and cultural causes and effects. Knowledge of changes in mood produced by chemicals is growing. "Cultural deprivation" and its effects are in the popular press. As more understanding of the interrelations of these four factors emerges,

29

the true foundations of mental health will become clearer, and better understanding of the seemingly endless variety of individuality will develop. There are many things we now know, but there are so many yet to be learned that I doubt that anyone can today, in complete confidence, define a practical course that will assure mental health for everyone. To use Elton Mayo's terms, we have now come a long way from the "traditional society" in which the farmer's son inevitably became a farmer. Instead we have moved far into an "adaptive society," minus the comforting anchors and roots of tradition, requiring endless adaptation to an almost dizzying rate of change. The ability to adapt to change is one of the hallmarks of mental health.

It is important to note that mental health carries no connotation of loss of individuality or conformity to some concept of an "average man." Individuality is a part of the very essence of human beings. A search for an average man in an industry is as absurd as a search for an "average" book in a library. All books have covers, pages, and words arranged in meaningful sequence. But there is an infinite variety of arrangement of words and of the meanings conveyed. And there is a similar variety among human beings.

Also, the "normal range" has a blurred periphery. There are some psychoneurotics and obsessive-compulsive personalities whom supervision in industry would classify among their very best workers because these individuals set such a high standard of performance for themselves. They work well in industry, but at considerable cost and discomfort to themselves.

And now to a significant question for which too few facts are as yet available: What is the relationship between mental health and mental illness and the work environment? If the occurrence of emotional problems of greater or lesser severity approaches 100 percent in a long enough time span, it is patently impossible for industry to contemplate conducting its affairs only with employees who are never subject to emotional problems. While it is expected that—at the time of the employment consideration—the individual who is sufficiently out of touch with reality to merit hospitalization will probably be screened out, it is equally expectable that those who will be employed will bring with them the whole variety of human foibles and frailties. There will be some whose degree of emotional stability is enviable. There will be some who have been wobbling along through life on such an uneven keel that most of their energy is used to keep their own boat bailed out with little energy left over for working and living. The remainder, including you and me, will be somewhere between these two extremes.

In a gross sort of way, it is possible for industry to match people and job assignments—the introspective, creative individual may do well in the research department and the hearty, gregarious person may be better suited for the sales department. But when one considers the infinite variety of individualities and our serious inability to measure the emotional content of each job and job situation, it seems highly unlikely that a complete matching of each individual's specific psychiatric make-up with the emotional factors of each job assignment can be accomplished, at least with the present state of the art.

Lacking specifics then, we are led to generalize; and generalizations are always hazardous. Regarding the individual, we have said that—beyond Freud's concepts of the psychological molding of infancy and childhood—there are in fact four factors—biological, psychological, societal, and cultural —which interplay in cause and effect relationships in personality structuring. The same four factors can readily be identified in the industrial setting and have a bearing on the emotional climate in an industry, a company or a specific job, and further add formidably to the complexity of the subject. During the past several decades, there have been and continue to be many attempts to extract from these complexities certain "truths" that have broad applicability.

Adam Smith contended that the thing that moved and satisfied men was money. Current theories accept this with some reservations, but consider that other things of equal or perhaps greater importance must be in the mix. The famous Hawthorne experiment suggested that attention to the human aspects of the work situation was more important to productivity than the adequacy of light at the work bench. The theory of the "hierarchy of needs" is receiving increasingly wide acceptance, namely, that as the more basic needs of man are fulfilled, needs of a higher order become dominant. Another theory divides human needs into satisfiers and motivators, meaning that fulfillment of certain needs will lead only to satisfaction and not to motivation; other needs are involved with motivating. The theory of "participatory management" has had its ups and downs in recent years. As with other current theories, this one, too, probably contains a nugget of truth; but its application needs more study, and it is too simplistic to be the whole answer. The management theory of Macgregor's "X and Y," Blake's managerial grid, the use of so-called sensitivity training, and many others have their proponents, indeed, their ardent supporters today.

There is a truisim in medicine to the effect that when a great many types of treatment are in use for a condition, the true etiology of the disorder is unknown and the kinds of treatments available are not wholly effective. This is undoubtedly true regarding interpersonal relations and "emotional climates" in industry. Nevertheless the fact that so many theories have been developed and so much attention is being given to these matters is salutary and one can hope that a continuance of these efforts will be productive.

We have said that an employed group contains the variety of foibles and frailties of human beings and that these varying personality characteristics come with the individual to the job. And we have emphasized the individuality of individuals. A monotonous job can be terribly disturbing to one individual, while the same monotony can act as a soothing sedative to another. This is not to say, however, that the emotional climate of the work situation is not important. One can conceive of a climate that is conducive to maximum job satisfaction and optimal productivity as well as minimally disturbing to the emotional state of employees, or even emotionally supportive. Conceiving of such a climate and knowing how to produce it, however, are two different things.

Knowledge in the whole spectrum of the behavioral sciences is growing. Studies range from the microbiology of nervous tissue and computer simulation of nerve networks, the rapidly emerging science of psychopharmacology and clinical studies of various emotional states, to studies of group phenomena by psychologists, psychiatrists, and sociologists. Industries have departments for personnel research. Universities continue their studies of animals and man in controlled and manipulated laboratory environments. But to a growing extent, universities and industries are joining hands to study man at work in the actual work environment. Much knowledge that is useful can be expected to come from this important symbiosis.

We are in the midst of a "knowledge explosion" in all fields, including the behavioral sciences. As our understandings and insights increase, we face a growing awareness of the need for a loom on which to weave all this into a useful fabric.

4   Mental Health at Work

Stanley F. Yolles

The federal government plays an increasingly significant role in mental health research, training, and services. In the recent reorganization of the United States Public Health Service, the National Institute of Mental Health was divorced from its sister institutes and elevated to bureau status reporting directly to the Surgeon General. Through grants and contracts to individuals and institutions, much of the current research and training in psychiatry and the behavioral sciences in the United States today is funded through this federal agency. Through regional centers, it provides mental health services to communities. Administering the Community Mental Health Centers Act, NIMH is stimulating the development of hundreds of contemporary community agencies to provide therapeutic and preventive mental health services throughout the country.

It is fortunate that Stanley F. Yolles, director of the Institute, has for some years been interested in occupational psychiatry. As a member of the Committee on Occupational Psychiatry of the American Psychiatric Association, he coauthored the book The Mentally Ill Employee. *As an administrator, he has management responsibility for the staff of NIMH. He therefore writes from the perspective of psychiatrist, executive, and chief federal spokesman for mental health. I asked Dr. Yolles to describe the federal government's interest in occupational mental health. What activi-*

ties are being supported by NIMH that relate to this field? What may be future federal involvement in this area? Are there activities, programs, or support that an employer may seek from NIMH in support of the mental health of his employees? How can a community mental health center contribute?

The past three decades have seen Stanley Yolles in three distinct and rewarding careers. Prior to the Second World War, he was well along on a career as a parasitologist. His work in that profession successfully culminated, however, in his role as commanding officer of the Sector Epidemiological Laboratory in the British West Indies. From parasitology, he turned directly to medicine, and received his medical degree from New York University in 1950. Soon after, he began his subsequent and continuous association with the U.S. Public Health Service. After psychiatric training, he served as staff psychiatrist, then associate director and director of the Mental Health Study Center of NIMH. This was the finale of his active clinical practice of psychiatry. In August 1960 he became associate director for Extramural Programs of NIMH, beginning a principally administrative role. Rising rapidly, he served as deputy director and acting director and in December 1964 assumed his present responsibility as director of NIMH. In addition, he is a member of the Mental Health Council of the American Medical Association, and of the Board of Editors of Psychiatry Digest. *He is a Fellow of the American Association for Advancement of Science, the American Psychiatric Association, and the American Public Health Association.*

At the outset of any work assignment, a man is asked to state his qualifications. I should like to do this—using the first person indicative—as a quick way to indicate that our mutual concern over the mental health of the American population can only bring positive results through the activity of an interlocking partnership.

The National Institute of Mental Health is the federal

agency responsible for federal support of mental health re-search, for the training of manpower, and for the delivery of mental health services. Therefore, as its director, I have the opportunity and the responsibility to administer this sup-port. Mental health *is* my work.

The Institute, in carrying out the intent of the administra-tion and Congress, employs a staff of some 1500 persons, so that its director is privy to all the joys and woes of an em-ployer operating within the complexities of government and the regulations of the Civil Service Commission.

In furthering the development of a comprehensive pro-gram of mental health services, it is the prime responsibility of the medical profession generally and the medical spe-cialty of psychiatry in particular to make sure that such serv-ices are medically sound as well as financially solvent. Therefore, as a psychiatrist, I am concerned that the profes-sion acts to face the issues before it and establishes policies to meet its modern responsibilities.

But what of industry? What do I know about that?

By 1964, three million men and women, comprising 4 per-cent of the total labor force in the United States, were em-ployed in health services, constituting one of the Nation's largest and fastest-growing enterprises. These millions are employed by government agencies at all levels, by nonprofit health facilities and agencies, and by private industry and commercial firms.

Since the health services enterprise has developed until very recently without conscious planning, its separate parts often have conflicting interests. Increasingly, however, this service enterprise is learning that the demands upon it are so great that its diverse interests must be brought together in a common working partnership.

I am professionally involved, as is the entire U.S. Public Health Service, in negotiating methods to achieve cooperation as they relate to federal support of community health services.

The manufacturers of goods, as well as the purveyors of health services, are concerned with mental health and the business community. This concern has been expressed by President of the National Association of Manufacturers W.P. Gullander. It is his belief, he stated recently, that one of the objectives of NAM is to promote "sound industrial answers to essentially social problems."

Certainly, from any point of view, the improvement of the mental health of our population is a social problem. To state the problem simply, the emerging field of occupational mental health is concerned with both the psychiatrically ill employee and with elements in the work environment that stimulate mentally healthy behavior.

A few people have been working on this for many years and I commend to your attention a review of the field by Dr. Alan McLean, published by the National Clearinghouse for Mental Health Information.[1]

But only recently has any significant concern been shown by industry over the fact that the social and psychological troubles of employees need to be recognized and prevented, as well as treated. It is through enlightened self-interest that industry is now becoming aware that the relationship between a man's work and his mental health is basic: both to human satisfactions and to industrial productivity.

Most industrial mental health programs have been established *after* something went wrong. In this they have much in common with treatment of mental illness *after* the crisis. In both instances, our view though understandable has been too narrow.

However, one industrial firm with which I am familiar

[1] Occupational Mental Health: Review of An Emerging Art, Public Health Service Publication No. 1469 (Bethesda, Md., 1966).

recently met a specific problem with an eye to prevention, as well as treatment. Although simple in concept, the decision and recent results appear to be an effective example of mental health at work.

The work situation in this company had become so bad that ten thousand written grievances were on file, awaiting decision at the top.

Out of mutual desperation, the director of industrial relations and the vice president of the union agreed to collaborate in establishing a better procedure for handling grievances.

At first, they divided the ten thousand grievances—one for you, and one for me, and one for the wastebasket. But that left each of them with more than three thousand grievances and this, they agreed, was no procedure. Finally they worked out a plan.

All grievances, they said, must be settled *today,* by the two people directly involved. These two were at liberty to call upon any persons they chose for consultation, but the aggrieved parties were present during the consultations and accepted the results. Under this procedure, everyone in the firm began to feel that putting a grievance in writing represented a sign of failure.

They discovered further that when complaints were discussed and resolved immediately, absenteeism, employee turnover, arguments, and accident rates went down.

In effect, the company's director of industrial relations and the vice president of the union were acting as behavioral scientists. They were investigating man's behavior and putting the results of their research to specific use. This is, of course, a very specific example of behavioral research undertaken to solve a specific human problem of personal relations on the job.

After all, industry can document the fact that two-thirds

of its job loss is caused by personal factors; that 80 to 90 percent of its accidents are based on the "human factor"; that employee turnover, absenteeism, accidents, scrap, and alcoholism are major problems. These seem to be—and actually are—specific problems in a sense, to be dealt with pragmatically.

But in the last few years, mental health professionals have been taking a wider view in their search for the answers to the question "Why does man behave as he does?" and some of what we find has direct bearing on mental health in the business community. This, I submit, can be part of Mr. Gullander's "industrial answer" to essentially social problems.

We are beginning to realize that mental health is the sum total of the quality of a man's environment, the quality of his life and the way he lives it. This, of course, includes a man's life at work.

In its research program, the NIMH supports research in the etiology, diagnosis, treatment, prevention, and control of mental illness and the promotion of mental health.

In our research to prevent mental illness and to improve mental health, one can say that events have moved into the laboratory and that the laboratory has become the world. I need not tell you that our complex, uneven, crowded, and frenetic society has achieved some horrors about which we need more knowledge.

The process of American urbanization and industrialization is affecting all the United States. The problems of metropolitan areas are problems of stress, of sharing, of overlap, of increased leisure time. Automating industry is creating surplus manpower that is relatively unskilled and undereducated.

The problem for the mental health professional is, of course, not the assumption of total responsibility for the facts of urbanization and industrialization, or for their administration. Our research problem is to analyze these conditions as they affect man's behavior and his health. It is no longer enough for us to search for the causes of mental illness after the illness has developed. We must turn to the basic question: How do you prevent an illness from starting?

We must learn how to intervene—at the places of stress and the times of crisis—with individuals, with groups, and with communities to prevent mental illness.

In this context, it matters very little what the motive is. If mental illness can be prevented in a family, that family will be spared the cost of such illness. If it can be prevented within a group—such as a group of employees within an industry—then that industry gains, in proportion to the individual gains of its workers. The same results can accrue within a community.

The federal government is quite definitely in the business of helping communities provide mental health services for all their residents. But that involvement is one of *support*. The essential ingredients of this program of mental health services must be and are being provided by public and private resources within local communities; this includes the business and industrial community.

There was a time in this country when every family drew its own water and put out its own fires. That time is long past for most of us. Today, just as our forebears levied taxes on themselves and gave voluntary contributions to provide light, fire and police protection and clean water for their towns, so are we—somewhat belatedly—arriving at the belief that the provision of mental health services is also a responsibility of each community.

This chapter cannot tell the whole story of the development of these community mental health centers. It is an exciting series of events and a story that is just beginning.

The format and procedures for establishing these centers have been achieved.

Approximately two hundred and fifty of them have already been provided with federal support and other hundreds will open their doors within the next few years. My point is that these centers are now becoming available and accessible for use by all residents of a community in a variety of ways. I should like to discuss here some of the ways in which they can be of use to the business and industrial segments of communities in which they operate.

To mention the simplest and most direct use first, these centers are being organized to provide a continuity of care for every person who needs such care: from emergency treatment, to forestall or treat a psychiatric crisis, to help in maintaining a person on the job by providing the kind of therapy and treatment he needs when he needs it.

For the first time in many communities, residents will have quality mental health services, provided at a price they can pay. Some of these centers are being planned from the ground up; others are being organized around existing facilities, such as general hospitals, with the addition of other services. And all of them, to qualify for federal support, must provide educational and consultative services to their communities.

The benefits of these services to industries within the community are limited only to the extent of their use *by* industry.

If a firm decides to establish its own mental health program—of whatever type—the consultative staff of the center is available to it. Such a liaison can be developed in many ways, but as a concrete example, I should like to cite the specific problem of alcoholism and the misuse of alcohol. Industry recognizes the problem, certainly, and must have help in solving it.

Community mental health centers will treat alcoholics and problem drinkers. Their administrative and treatment procedures will differ, because there is, to date, no single answer to this extremely perplexing condition. However, the center staff will assume its share of responsiblity for treatment. Its educational and consultative staff will, upon request, work with industries to establish and develop industrial programs to control alcoholism.

Nowhere in the nation have we as yet applied enough knowledge, energy, and funds to attack the problems resulting from alcohol misuse, but we have now arrived at a point of no return; and recent events indicate that we are about to achieve something besides talk concerning the subject.

The people of the country, at all levels and in all pursuits, are concerned. At NIMH, more individual letters are addressed to us asking for help in this area than on any other single subject.

It is our intention to make the results of research and experimental treatment, counseling, and control immediately available to persons who can put that knowledge to use. It is also our intention to support training of more persons competent to work in this field. Granted, this is only a beginning. But it is a beginning that can become a potent ally of industry in our common need to control the drinking habits of our productive population.

I have indicated, in the past few pages, only a minute fraction of the services community mental health centers can give to individuals and to communities, but they are demonstrable. All you have to do is try them on for size and they will grow with your demands and your support.

That support, of course, is crucial. The actual establishment of community-based services for the mentally ill, as a concept and as a reality, was vastly accelerated by the adoption in 1963 of the Community Mental Health Centers Act.

The implications of this legislation were tremendous. As a nation, we admitted that our treatment of the mentally ill had been, at worst, inhumane, and at best, less than adequate in the light of our knowledge. But in pragmatic actuality, the Centers Act, with its 1965 amendments, provides only partial support through federal funding of some of the costs of construction and of the initial staffing of the centers.

The larger share of the costs of establishing, maintaining, and operating these centers will be met in the community. State, county, and municipal governments and the private sector are becoming involved in funding mechanisms of wide variety as each community adapts its own resources to its needs and interests in providing mental health centers. There is an infinite variety of these funding patterns; and industries are participating in many communities, as they take a realistic look at their own needs.

Industry is also contributing to the planning of many of these centers, as well as their funding, in direct and indirect ways.

One of the changes within our changing urban communities is the fact that many community leaders are newcomers. Often they come into a community as representatives of large industries, trained in the new techniques of management. Their power rests on interpersonal relationships and the use of managerial information and techniques that have come into widespread use quite recently.

Both as representatives of their firms and as civic-minded volunteers, they are becoming a significant force in the planning and sponsorship of community services, including mental health services. And although health is not their primary concern, they will increasingly put the stamp of their abilities and interests on the quality of services provided within the area in which they work and live and rear their families. This group, probably as much as any other, will

43

cause the development of the emerging public-private partnership into a community services pattern of benefit to all residents and all industries.

I mentioned earlier that individual psychiatrists and the profession of psychiatry must face some issues and establish some policies to meet modern community responsibilities of leadership. I should like to expand that comment.

The modern industrialist is learning to participate in a wider variety of community affairs than his grandfather did. This has taken time and a change in attitude, for the American industrialist is, traditionally, an independent man who was once quite sure that he could go it alone.

In these qualities, he has much in common with the psychiatrist—who also, traditionally, did indeed go it alone.

Psychiatry is a new medical specialty. It concerns itself with the minds of men, which, as any industrialist knows, are complex. For years, therefore, the individual psychiatrist treated his individual patients in an even more personal way than did his colleagues in other specialties of medicine, for an upset mind is often more alarming than an upset stomach.

In the past ten or twenty years, however, some psychiatrists have learned that it is possible to think of the mental health of groups of persons as effectively as they once thought of the mental health of one patient. The resultant concept is known as community psychiatry. Its practitioners base their treatment on the idea that mental health is public health and that the control and prevention of mental illness can best be sought through public health methods.

The practice of community psychiatry will undoubtedly continue to develop, but even the psychiatrist who recognizes the exciting challenge of a modern community practice sometimes finds it difficult to assume his share of organizational as well as medical leadership in the community.

He must do this, however, if the mental health services

program is to be of sound value to the community and of solid worth to a large number of individual patients.

It is true that the acceptance of the psychiatrist in business and industry has been slow. Industrialists have sometimes said that psychiatrists have no knowledge of private enterprise; that they belittle practical knowledge in the field of human relations as used by industrialists in their daily work with their employees.

But for every industrialist who rejected the contributions psychiatrists could make toward improving the working environment, there were others who established mental health programs and learned the supportive value of psychiatric consultation. Since the various types of programs are discussed extensively in other chapters, I shall not enumerate them.

I shall spend the balance of this paper telling you something of the ways in which programs supported by the National Institute of Mental Health may be helpful to individual business firms.

As I have indicated, the Institute staff, both in Washington and in our regional offices, is available to you for consultation. Institute activity in helping to survey and stimulate coverage of mental illnesses in prepaid and other insurance programs is continuing. As many of you know, such benefits are currently being negotiated by management and labor as fringe benefits in some industrial contracts.

The provisions in the automotive industry's contract, providing coverage for psychiatric illness, provide a case in point. In order to implement those provisions, the Institute awarded a grant to the American Psychiatric Association and the United Automobile Workers that made it possible for them to survey and coordinate available resources in order that these treatment benefits could actually be made available.

Most of the current research and service programs supported by the Institute are of benefit to industrial firms, as they are to all parts of our society.

It is worth a comment, I think, that industry seems still quite reluctant to initiate the kinds of mental health research that only industry can do. Any firm possesses data on which solid conclusions about absenteeism, accidents, turnover, and other problem situations could be based; but few industries are as yet willing to take a sharp look at these data.

This sort of research is badly needed, if we are to learn anything specific and significant about relationships, say, between morale, productivity, and safety.

I have deliberately refrained until now from commenting on industry's attitudes toward persons who have been treated for mental illness. Some employers are more enlightened than others in this matter. I am sorry to say that the federal government, although its attitudes as an employer are improving in this regard, still has a long way to go.

This is an area in which both public and private employers *must* cooperate to effect change. For, with today's treatment techniques, we encourage people to seek psychiatric help, on the one hand, and penalize them by rejecting, or at least questioning, their employment applications if they state that they have received such treatment. Such attitudes are neither humane, logical, nor common sense, in terms of the realities of the modern world.

I have said very little about the costs of mental illness to the nation, to the individuals who are themselves victims of psychiatric disorders, and to their families and friends. These huge costs cannot be truly measured; they involve costs of care and treatment, still largely financed by public funds; and there are other costs that can only be considered in terms of personal anguish and loss of an opportunity to live and work productively.

The costs of mental illness, in terms of dollars, can be lowered as community mental health centers provide short-term treatment and cut back the number of beds needed for mental patients in long-term, custodial facilities.

Our major goal, however, must be the goal of prevention. This, of course, cannot be entirely achieved through the establishment of occupational mental health programs within industry. But programs to improve the population's mental health at work can be significant factors in working toward the objective of prevention of mental illness.

Since we live in a working society, in the largest sense, all our mental health is "occupational" mental health. It is to our mutual advantage to promote the mental health of all our population by improving the quality of American life. Our motives may stem from compassion or from a need for human productivity, but our success will profit all of us.

5   Management Views Psychiatric Disability

Marvin M. Wedeen

*Marvin Wedeen is in charge of both marketing and labor rela-
tions for the Dellwood Dairy Company, a medium-sized organization well known in the New York City area. I asked him to
provide a management viewpoint on disability and rehabilitation
of employees who have had a psychiatric disorder. Prior to undertaking this assignment, he had really given little thought to the
subject. As a sound executive, however, I knew his experience
would provide a fresh approach.*

*Mr. Wedeen's orientation is apparent in this chapter. He is a
member of the Greater New York Milk Dealers Labor Committee
and an employer trustee of two teamsters union-management
pension and welfare funds. Experienced in representing management's point of view at the bargaining table, he defines the problems facing the smaller employer who is considering a program of
care for the psychiatrically disabled employee. Further, after out-
lining all possible objections to employer action, he concludes
that companies must assume some responsibilities and that business itself can stimulate the community's medical profession to
provide it with competent guidance. This visualization of a management role beyond the immediate suggests a sophistication to
be found throughout this chapter.*

Readers in the New York City area will recognize the advertising slogan "From Dellwood with Love" developed under Mr. Wedeen's administration. I am not sure that this identification necessarily personifies the man, but it does suggest that we are reading a man who is both a hardheaded business negotiator and one able to incorporate his feelings at an intellectual level.

I asked him: From the industrial relations point of view, what concerns does management legitimately have in the mental health of its employees? How does management view the applicant with a history of psychiatric disorder? How about the employee? How far should an employer go in attempting to rehabilitate an individual with a psychiatric disorder?

This paper will examine the subject of mental health in the business community from the standpoint of a general management executive. If the average manager were asked his attitude toward a new program to handle disabling psychiatric disorders of employees, his first reaction would be to balk at the addition of a new employee program. Management is slow to adopt change, particularly when it involves a new benefit. Unless the change offers a benefit for the company or is a matter of the least threatening evil, management is generally conservative.

There are often good reasons for sitting back and waiting instead of diving in to develop a new policy or program. In the case of psychiatric disorders there are a number of problems that must first be resolved before a manager can think constructively. Most managers have no clear concepts of what is involved. It is hard to draw comparisons between physical disability and mental disability. For a supervisor to respond to an employee with a broken leg or a cut finger is simple. If the injury occurs on the job, he seeks first aid or emergency medical care to limit the injury and assist the employee. He then notifies his insurance carrier. The same injury off the job poses no great problem either.

Contrast this with a mental breakdown or a case of alcohol addiction. It's not easy for a manager to understand what is happening or whether this is a valid medical disability. He should seek professional advice, but he may not realize how to go about it. In a middle-sized company such as mine, family doctors serve management and employees as the first line medical advisors. Unless the family doctor has psychiatric training or has established liaison with a psychiatrist, as is often the case with an orthopedic surgeon, cardiologist, and gynecologist, he may not get to the root of an emotional problem, and therefore, may not be able to advise management or the employee of what is really happening or how serious the illness really is. Because the family doctor frequently does not help management understand the role of the psychiatrist, management does not seek out such aid in the early stages of a disability. Consequently, most emotional problems go well down the track before they are identified as such.

MANAGEMENT RESISTANCE

The resistance of management to company mental health programs is further fortified by the fear of the high cost of psychiatric care. Most managers still feel that getting into this area is opening a Pandora's box of high cost to the company. Insurance companies put a high rate on psychiatric coverage in major medical policies. We hear of the many office visits involved in psychiatric treatment and can only conclude that this offers an inefficient approach to the treatment of large numbers of employees with the present supply of psychiatrists and great uncertainty as to the outcome of treatment. Assuming legal and financial responsibility for psychiatric disability can be expensive. For this reason alone, there is, logically enough, a tendency to avoid company involvement until the last possible moment.

As we look at the recent developments in the area of compensation cases, however, it becomes apparent that we soon may have only two choices. One is to accept a psychiatric claim on the basis of medical evidence as compensable. The other is to controvert the claim through the boards and the courts. Once we accept the newer legal definitions that broaden employer responsibility, the cost of care will encourage us to seek ways to rehabilitate employees. In doing so we will be reducing the long-range cost of a disabled employee who is unable to seek other employment until rehabilitated.

ACTION NOW?

In spite of all these reasons to support a position of foot dragging, there *are* valid considerations for doing something now. Today there are increasing needs for solving the problems that confront management when an employee develops a psychiatric disorder. When mental illness results in the loss of services of a valuable employee, many pressures come to play on his employer. His skill may be important to group productivity. Or, the lack of help to a key employee may imply management disinterest, which can then lead to a breakdown of the employee's concern for the problems of management.

The type of company help may vary from financing part of the medical costs to carrying the employee on the payroll until he is able to return to work. The company may help in rehabilitation by finding work for the employee and accepting less productivity for a period of time. It is conceivable that a concerned company may wind up with a number of less productive employees while a competitor who ruthlessly ignores all responsibility will avoid this type of overhead expense.

Sometimes the decisions of how much help to offer are made for the employer by the type of business he is in and by its particular financial situation. A growing business can frequently absorb a few less productive employees who need partial rehabilitation while a declining business may find itself stuck with no one but incompetents with seniority rights if it assumed an obligation of rehabilitation in the case of physical or mental illness. For example, how many disabled employees can a small distribution company with thirteen salesmen support?

I believe most small companies today would say "replace" rather than "rehabilitate" an employee if the companies were convinced that rehabilitation would be lengthy and the degree of success uncertain. Only when finding a satisfactory replacement for the disabled is difficult will rehabilitation be seriously accepted.

Another factor motivating management is the need to resolve the question, When is an employee too disabled to work? When an employee or his union questions whether a man is disabled, the employer is asked to employ the worker even though he may become sicker and may cause unnecessary waste. This type of dispute can be handled in union contracts. A provision can be established whereby an employee is required to submit medical evidence of his ability to return to work, and where this evidence may be challenged by the employer's doctor. In case of a medical dispute between doctors, each agrees on a third expert as the final arbitrator whose decision is binding.

When the question of disability involves economic loss on the part of either employee or employer, both expert medical decisions and expert treatment are desirable. Management initiative may be an important element in saving cost in this area. Doctors may not be as helpful in all such cases as management would wish. I recently sat on a jury that listened to the evidence of two psychiatrists, one for the employer and one for the employee. One claimed the employee was psychologically damaged for life and could no longer work, while the other equally qualified expert claimed that the employee was capable of returning to work. With such added confusion in union-management relations, employers must find ways to arm themselves with competent psychiatric advice and offer ways to provide competent care and rehabilitation so that the cost of adverse decisions may be minimized.

MANAGEMENT-UNION CONFLICT

Once management overcomes its reluctance and seeks solutions to employee mental illness, it must move carefully to avoid further difficulties. In the case of company initiated psychiatric counseling, someone will invariably question if the psychiatrist will interpret employee disability with a management bias rather than with primary concern for rehabilitation of his patient. For companies with union contracts one must question if the program should be a supplement or a prelude to contract provisions. Will it be an extra benefit that the union expects from management without contract recognition and without economic credit in a future settlement? Did General Motors initiate its psychiatric program before the UAW negotiated psychiatric benefits, or did they wait to have this program become part of the total package of benefits to be costed for the contract settlement? I suspect the latter. But I ask this question because I find unions want programs that will save their members money they have spent in the past. If members do not feel that the proposed benefit is of particular value, they will require their negotiators to buy another benefit of similar cost to the employer that has greater employee appeal. The company may thus have two benefits when planning to finance only one. Will the instituted program, once established, lock the employer into a commitment for the future, or will there be an escape hatch that permits management to alter, improve, or discontinue it as its needs change?

INSURANCE CONSIDERATIONS

I have tried to show that there are reasons for management resistance to new programs; yet there are many immediate needs to do something about psychiatric treatment and re-habilitation. Overseeing this debate are broader pressures that are mounting and that will place the employer in a position where he must be able to understand employee psychiatric disability *in order to exist*. The broadening legal interpretation of disability will rapidly enlarge the responsibility of management. There is no question that for economic reasons management will continue to resist having the costs of psychiatric disorder paid by its company insurance carrier. In time this may become a debate about whether it is paid by the disability insurance carrier or the compensation insurance carrier.

While resistance and debate continue, there will be innovating companies and unions that will establish welfare benefits leaving no doubt that employees with psychiatric disorders will be treated and rehabilitated. We have seen this innovation in medical benefits, starting with twenty-one–day Blue Cross plans and we now have very comprehensive medical-surgical programs. In New York City, management and the teamster unions are testing a comprehensive group medical program similar to the Kaiser plan in the hope of providing better care at lower cost to the employer. As this happens, we find that union leaders are becoming educated in the field of medical and psychiatric care. In many instances union representatives are better equipped to discuss these problems than their counterparts in management.

Once the innovators have set the pattern, the pressures on other employers to copy or find substitutes develop. Sometimes it is a question of employers competing for skilled labor or unions competing for equal benefits. Eventually the government will be asked to provide similar benefits for employees not represented by unions or those working in marginal businesses that cannot afford such benefits without government subsidy. Medicare is a good example of government involvement. Although Medicare was proposed many years ago, once it was blocked in Congress, unions sought the same type of benefit through negotiation. The milk industry in New York, as a result of such a negotiation, provided medical benefits for pensioned employees beginning in 1962. I am sure our employees and other employees who were being pensioned with medical care financed in part by the employer helped to swing political pressure for universal care to all older and retired workers.

If and when government provides universal psychiatric care, the increase in activity will create the need for upgrading treatment facilities. Government, employers, and employees will all have to contribute to improving these facilities just as Medicare has encouraged and accelerated examination of our hospitals and nursing homes in local communities.

CONSIDERATIONS FOR THE EMPLOYER

As the care and rehabilitation of employees proceeds, management will become more active in the development of mental health programs. I have set down some suggestions for the small and medium-sized company to follow (my personal experience makes me more familiar with these sizes then with the giant company).

1. Psychiatric care should be part of good medical care. It will be too confusing to set up a separate department outside the system now used for physical disabilities.

2. Good medical care must include preventive programs including early diagnosis and treatment. The 1962 Group Health Insurance study by Helen Hershfield Avnet suggested that a psychiatric care program will encourage earlier detection and treatment. The GM-UAW program may confirm this.

3. Most psychiatric disability is not job connected. Consideration of the work situation's aggravating a pre-existing condition focuses too much on the employer and too little on the family. Instead of waiting for everyone to pin the responsibility for care and rehabilitation on the employer, each community should develop a comprehensive program for action to include:

     a. A state financed "second injury fund" to handle the cost of care and rehabilitation in preexisting cases where care and rehabilitation go beyond six months. (The present limit in New York State is two years with a physical disability. The fund is financed through insurance companies; thus the employer assumes the full cost.)

     b. Construction of psychiatric wings in local general hospitals with both in-patient and out-patient care. These units could serve as part of community mental health centers.

c. Establishment of community sheltered workshops that provide transition to full employment.

d. Encouragement of specific industries to locate in the community to provide employment for the individual who is released from a sheltered workshop, yet cannot return to his original employer. (Incentives for such businesses must be provided, possibly by allowing tax abatement, or providing psychiatric nursing and work supervision at community expense.)

CONCLUSIONS

Each company program for psychiatric care and rehabilitation will develop at a different time and at a different pace. Management should and must initiate ideas so that community programs will be helpful to the industrial community. Business representation can stimulate the community's medical profession to provide competent guidance. Furthermore, management can help enlist broad community support by recruiting employees to work on community programs. This type of involvement and commitment is similar to that which management would assume in any other problem situation. Take, for example, the case of a company that operates a small manufacturing plant in a rural community. If there were not sufficient community fire protection to safeguard the plant, I am sure a company-sponsored volunteer fire brigade would be nurtured to avoid loss of life and property and thus reduce insurance premiums. In the same way, once need has motivated management to provide psychiatric care and rehabilitation, it will have to muster all its resources to make the program effective.

II

Approaches
to Industrial
Mental Health

6 Clinical Programs

Simon L. Auster

A child psychiatrist, Simon Auster is director of the Fairfax-Falls Church Mental Health Center in Falls Church, Virginia. In this position, he is responsible for psychiatric diagnosis and treatment, primarily with children, both directly and through the supervision of his staff members. At the Center, he has instituted regular consultation with area nursery school teachers around classroom problems. In addition, he consults with the staffs of community agencies and services. Rarely does this include consultation with local industry.

Why, then, should I invite a child psychiatrist and clinic director to contribute a paper on mental health in industry? The answer, of course, lies within the complexities of Simon Auster's personality. His background is broad and diverse for such a recent graduate (A.B. summa cum laude, Yeshiva University, 1952; M.D., New York University, 1956). In addition to sound training in psychiatry and in child psychiatry, he served as consultant to the National Training Laboratories of the National Education Association. The NTL programs are widely used in industry for human relations training of management people. Since 1961, he has been a member of the Commission of Human Resources of the Washington Center for Metropolitan Studies.

Since 1963, Dr. Auster has spent two days each week as con-

sultant in occupational mental health at the National Institute of Mental Health. For three years his primary responsibility has been to survey occupational mental health activities in the United States. He has not restricted his studies to psychiatric programs in industry and labor, but has also included a review of the relationship between work and mental health, a study of the mental health significance of automation, retirement, and unemployment, and a study of the influence of work design and organizational structure as they relate to mental health and the mental disorder. He is also a member of the National Institute of Mental Health Task Force on Voluntary Psychiatric Insurance, and, in this capacity, is studying the UAW program discussed by Mr. Glasser in chapter fifteen.

I asked Dr. Auster to describe recent industrial mental health programs that have successfully brought to bear contemporary concepts from psychiatry, occupational medicine, and clinical psychology. First, what is the "clinical" approach? How does it differ from that of the behavioral sciences? How may an interested employer originate a mental health program? Should it be part of an occupational medical activity, identified with a personnel function, or with the office of a chief executive? How can such activities be appropriately evaluated? Do they pay off economically?

The growing interest of the business community in the application of knowledge from other areas has resulted in a recognition of the importance of mental health to efficient operations. There is now an awareness of the magnitude of emotional problems in the work force at all levels, from porter to chief executive, which has raised questions about the dollar costs of such disabilities and opened the entire area of the reverse of occupational disability. That is productivity, creativity, and job satisfaction and the relationship of these functions to mental health.

In this paper I shall discuss some proposed solutions that have been developed through clinical programs. But the subject must be considered from several aspects. First, the nature of the clinical, as compared to the behavioral science approach, and the background and skills of the mental health clinician need to be understood. I will present some representative clinical programs and analyze them to provide a framework for understanding the issues to be discussed later. I am concerned with problems that are inherent in initiating and maintaining a mental health service in an organization. My discussion will therefore attempt to spell out major problems, clarify issues that contribute to creating and perpetuating the problems, and suggest solutions that have been found to be workable, either by resolving the difficulty itself, or simply by keeping it under control. I will conclude my discussion with some observations about staffing a program and a comment about how an organization should establish a program.

THE CLINICAL APPROACH

Webster defines the word "clinical" as pertaining to study or practice based on actual treatment and observation of patients, distinguishing it from experimental or laboratory study. This is an important distinction; while the scientist engaged in experimental and laboratory study is primarily concerned with increasing the body of knowledge so that planning and programming can be based on a solid foundation of carefully accumulated information, the clinician's prime concern is function (healthy as well as disordered). He is not an experimenter, although he may wish to systematically investigate problem areas or situations of unusual effectiveness that come to his attention in order to better understand them and be able to indicate the conditions that will alleviate or promote them. Unlike the behavioral scientist, whose goal is the development of knowledge, the goal of the clinician can usefully be conceptualized as that of putting himself out of business. This has several important corollaries. First, a good clinical service is more than a matter of therapists and patients or counselors and employees. Not only does the clinician have an obligation to treat those in difficulty, but he also must be concerned with the sources of difficulty and how they may be changed in such a way that the number of people developing problems is diminished and wherever possible healthy functioning is facilitated. Perhaps most important is the implication of this goal for the educational responsibilities of the clinician; it is incumbent upon him, wherever possible, to teach as much as he can of his knowledge and skills to those who, in their daily activities, are directly concerned with the functioning of others. In the business organization this would include physicians, supervisors, personnel officers, and even the company president. Depending on the group, this would focus on topics ranging from the early detection of emotional disturbance on the job and the medical and supervisory management of productive employees suffering from emotional disorder, to a more general consideration of the relationship between organizational climate and style and mental health. While in actual practice it is not very likely that any clinician, however good, would achieve this goal of making himself unnecessary, thinking of it in these terms allows the development of a framework that helps define the potential scope of the clinician's activities in treatment, prevention, and training.

Who is the mental health clinician? He is someone who has usually had training in one of the three traditional mental health disciplines—psychiatry, psychology, or social work. Because of their training, these professionals have developed their skills in understanding what in the past and present life experience of the individual affects his thoughts and feelings, and through them, his behavior. A good clinician is sensitive to the factors that can be stressful or supportive to a person, as well as knowledgeable about the symptoms of disorder. In the presence of disturbed functioning, through a careful exploration of the situation he can detect those areas of vulnerability in the personality that may be under stress at that moment, discover those factors that may be contributing to it, and suggest possible ways in which the stresses might be alleviated. It is important to understand that the clinician's suggestions in these situations can be no more than general; in the organizational setting, it is the supervisor and personnel man—those primarily responsible for the satisfactory operation of the enterprise—who must devise the specific solutions that meet the clinician's recommendations. In these situations, even more than where the issue is one of physical handicap, involvement of a union representative can greatly facilitate resolution of the difficulty.

To provide a concrete context for subsequent discussion, it will be useful to consider several programs that represent different types of clinical activities currently conducted in industry. Each of these is unique in one or several characteristics. Three of the programs are full-time and four part-time.

FULL-TIME CLINICAL PROGRAMS

Of the full-time programs, the first is in a multiplant operation staffed by two full-time and several part-time psychiatrists. Formally, the chief psychiatrist reports to the medical director, but in actual practice, he and his colleagues function with relative autonomy within the organization, having ready access to and being directly approached by senior management for assistance with a wide variety of problems, and broadly participating in personnel policy formulation. Perhaps a quarter of these clinicians' time is actually spent in direct patient responsibility. This is generally limited to evaluation and consultation with employees and supervisors; rarely, when it is apparent that several interviews will be sufficient for a primarily work-related problem, one of the consultants will see an employee for short-term treatment. In all other situations, recommendations are made to the employee and his supervisor, with referral of the former to private practitioners or community agencies for further treatment if necessary.

The bulk of the work is concerned with prevention. This is reflected in an ongoing exploration and evaluation of the work environment, including policies and practices either useful or potentially harmful to the individual and the organization. The results of these studies are discussed with the appropriate management personnel. The psychiatrists conduct educational programs for company physicians and for management. These are programs concerned with the early recognition of emotional disorder and the maintenance of the emotionally disturbed, yet productive, employee on the job. Basic information about mental health and the factors influencing it are discussed.

The second full-time program is conducted by a psychologist operating in a company medical department. It is identified as a counseling program but has traditionally participated in preemployment health examinations through the use of a variety of psychological tests. Originally established through the interest of a medical director who felt that preemployment physical examinations yielded inadequate information about the total health picture of the prospective employee, the counseling service has become an increasingly important aspect of its functioning. Evidence for this is to be found in the representative quality of its caseload, which includes people from all levels of the company, both patients who are self-referred and those referred by medical department physicians. While most of the time is spent in short-term counseling, the majority of those consulting the counselor are referred to other agencies in the community or to private practitioners for further counseling or psychotherapy. The company has an active alcoholism rehabilitation program that draws heavily on outside resources for treatment. The counseling service plays an important role in this program, arranging for the employee to take leave when necessary, maintaining contact with him when he is on leave, and providing follow-up counseling when he returns. Where difficulties are discovered that might be alleviated through consultation with a supervisor, the counselors are free to do this.

The third full-time program is staffed by social workers, and unlike the other two, operates autonomously within the organization. Originally reporting directly to the president, the counselors now report to one of the vice presidents. The program is almost entirely one of counseling, available to all employees at their request. Counselors are free to consult with supervisors wherever it seems indicated and they have the employee's permission. Occasionally, as an outgrowth of their counseling activities, an organizational problem will come to their attention; when this happens, they are free to discuss it with management. In a situation where major organizational changes are to be introduced, the counseling service is asked in advance to organize a program that would minimize the stress of the transition.

These three programs show the use of personnel from each of the mental health disciplines. They include one entirely within the medical department, both formally and functionally, one that is formally within the medical department, but functionally autonomous, and one where the program has a high degree of autonomy within the company, both formally and functionally.

The activities also show a wide range. At one extreme, we find a program whose functioning is entirely limited to counseling, organizational as well as individual. At the other we find a program broad in scope, concerned with prevention as its major focus. Between, we find a program primarily concerned with counseling, but involved in testing and evaluation as well.

PART-TIME CLINICAL PROGRAMS

The part-time programs to be described are naturally more limited in scope. They are all staffed by psychiatrists, perhaps as a consequence of the practice of part-time employment being more widespread among psychiatrists than among psychologists or social workers. It is also doubtless due to the characteristic predominant concern of these programs with direct service, rather than prevention. The first such program can be described very briefly, since it is an attenuated version of the first of the full-time programs described. The psychiatrist is responsible for some clinical evaluations and arranges for outside referrals when necessary, consulting with supervisors where it seems indicated. He does a limited amount of education and training, and devotes a part of his time to exploring areas of company practice that appear to be having deleterious effects on the employees. Unlike the full-time psychiatrists described earlier, however, he does not participate in policy-making.

In a second firm, the psychiatrist functions autonomously within the company and reports directly to the president. His major effort is devoted to an experimental program in improving on-the-job relations, consisting of regular, bi-weekly meetings with groups of middle management that focus on work-associated problems and interdepartmental communication. In addition to this, the psychiatrist is consulted by senior management and supervisory employees about personnel problems. Direct consultation is also available to all employees, but this element of the service is de-emphasized.

A third arrangement is typified by the presence of a part-time psychiatrist within the medical department, whose activities are concerned entirely with evaluation. There are no educational or preventive activities, nor is the psychiatrist free to consult with supervisory personnel regarding the management of a disturbed employee, this function being jealously guarded as a managerial prerogative. Where a disability evaluation is requested, the psychiatrist is restricted to addressing himself to the question of whether the man is disabled by his illness or not.

The final program is one where a panel of outside consultants is available to the medical director for referral when the medical department feels that further exploration into the emotional aspects of an individual's life is indicated. The work itself is primarily clinical, and, despite his being an outsider, the consultant has the freedom to discuss problems directly with supervisors if permission is given by the employee. On the rare occasions where the locus of the problem seems to be in the organization rather than in the individual, the consultant's impressions in this area are welcome and usually lead to an exploration of the situation.

It can be seen from these programs that part-time mental health activities in industry cover as wide a range as do full-time ones. In their relationships, they may be outside consultants drawn upon at the discretion of the medical director, they may have a position in the organization, usually in the medical department, and strictly limited to functioning within that department, they may be organizationally within the medical department but functionally free-wheeling, or they may be entirely autonomous. They may be limited in their area of concern to disability evaluation at one extreme or to organizational functioning at the other, or they may cover as wide a range of activities as do the full-time programs. Their part-time characteristic is the only one that uniformly differentiates them from the full-time programs, and not infrequently, this reflects nothing more than differences in the size of the employing company.

DEVELOPING A CLINICAL PROGRAM

With this description as a general background on the nature of clinical programs and with enough specific detail to provide a structure for thinking about program development, practical questions, and problems to be considered before establishing a program, can be examined. This part of the discussion will be concerned with questions of the financial justification of mental health programs, the structuring and organizational location of a program, the determination of suitable staff, the problems of gaining acceptance by the organization, and finally, the maintenance of a program once initiated.

The first question is that of financial justification as, aside from those that stem from fear and prejudice, this is the question most frequently raised when the possibility of introducing a mental health service into a corporation is broached. There is evidence to suggest that the question may itself be misleading. Several years ago, the National Opinion Research Center did a survey of industrial medical programs only to discover that, of the broad representation of industry they surveyed, less than half had any interest in a financial justification of their programs. The majority felt that, even though they might not be able to justify them in terms of cost, first, it was the responsibility of a corporation to provide this kind of service, and second, its availability contributed heavily to the maintenance of employee morale insofar as it reflected a concern on the part of management for the workers beyond being merely a pair of hands.

Approximately 45 percent of the companies, however, felt that they should be able to financially justify their medical services, and in fact were able to do so. In the provision of medical services, this is a fairly simple procedure, since the presence of a medical department is one of the factors considered in the determination of compensation insurance premiums. It is a very simple process, then, to determine the cost of maintaining a medical department and compare it with the savings on insurance premiums. In most cases, the presence of a medical department resulted in an actual saving for the company; in a somewhat smaller number, it did not seem to make much difference either way. In no cases did the medical department budget exceed the corporate saving in compensation premiums.

Although there have been several precedent-setting compensation decisions specifically concerned with the influence of emotional factors on disability, and there is evidence that this attitude of the courts is becoming more widespread, insurance carriers have shown no inclination to parallel their practice with medical services and reduce compensation premiums when a company maintains an active mental health program. While savings on insurance premiums may never cover the cost of a mental health service, it is possible to look for savings in other areas to do this. Some estimate of the net cost of a mental health service might be obtained through a study of the single element, turnover. If it can be shown that this is reduced in a company over a period of time following the establishment of a mental health service, then the savings can be weighed against the cost of the service. This reduction can be expected in several areas. A mental health service can be the critical factor that enables an employee who might otherwise leave the workforce to bridge the gap in returning to work after a period of absence due to emotional or physical illness or disabling injury. Such a service can reduce turnover through more careful and appropriate management of the borderline or emotionally disturbed employee. It might also have an impact on turnover as a result of changes in the organizational operation from supervisor education. Since the cost of employee replacement can range from several hundred to many thousands of dollars, when to this is added the direct cost to the company of disability payments, a mental health service would likely pay for itself even if it succeeds in retaining in the workforce only a limited number of employees who otherwise might have been lost. An effective program might similarly reduce the incidence and cost of absenteeism, accidents, and alcoholism, the traditionally accepted manifestations of emotional disturbance in the work setting. These areas, too, warrant more direct investigation than has been done until now; although this may be costly at first, it can be expected to pay for itself as the information obtained is applied in developing company policy.

It is important to understand that it is irrelevant whether the locus of the problem is the home or the job. A disabled worker is an expensive loss to a company whether his disability stems from stresses he is experiencing at home or stresses he is experiencing at work; minimally, the corporation's interest is the same.

Once the decision to initiate a mental health program is made, a number of issues must be settled before it can be implemented. The company must first decide roughly what kind of program it wants. Then the organizational placement needs to be determined. This should be one that will enable the program to function most effectively and with minimum disturbance of other groups. The professional training of the staff, whether psychiatry, psychology, or social work is a third question, and finally, the question of a full-time or part-time program must be settled.

In deciding the nature of a planned program, the company should take into consideration its particular requirements as determined by its size, organizational structure, corporate activity, the unique stresses inherent in its functioning, and how a mental health service might most usefully be integrated into its operation. The representative programs described above give some indication of the scope of program possibilities. A mental health service can be very restricted in its concerns, or it can be broad in scope. Its activities can range from direct clinical service to prevention. A clinical service can include such purely patient-oriented elements as diagnostic evaluation, consultation, and referral to outside resources, and direct counseling or treatment. It may have the freedom to go outside the relationship with the patient and communicate with appropriate supervisory personnel. In special circumstances it may be asked to develop, administer, and evaluate psychological tests. Moving into the area of prevention, programs might include such activities as physician education about emotional factors in illness and disability; supervisor instruction in mental health principles, in the identification of the indicators of emotional disorder, and in the routine handling of emotional problems on the job; and management seminars on social and industrial psychology and the implications of mental health principles for organizational practice. In some situations, clinical research could be an appropriate activity for a program. Finally, a mental health program can be a valuable source of recommendations in policy-planning.

Because of his skills and understanding of the factors that

influence human behavior, there is some temptation for management to turn to the mental health professional for help in the perennial problems of selection and promotion. This practice is usually unwise for several reasons: However skilled he may be in the evaluation of personality, the mental health professional has less understanding than a personnel man of the demands, the stresses, the difficulties, the satisfactions, the unique characteristics of a particular position. Furthermore, motivation and creativity, perhaps the most important elements in job success, are extremely difficult to evaluate and are closely related to the nature and structure of the work itself. The "fit" between individual and job is thus more likely to be better assessed by those more familiar with the substantive aspects of the work. Even were the professional particularly skilled at doing this work, having this authority would so seriously hamper the trust and open communication between himself and other employees necessary for his other activities, that it would be impossible for him to adequately discharge these other aspects of his job. The closest a mental health service should come to selection and promotion is through educational programs for personnel people and supervisors, which is imparted an understanding of those elements about an individual that are indicative of his psychological state and which have a high predictive value for behavior. These people can then apply this information in their own evaluations of applicants for employment.

Closely related to this question, and in many ways an even more thorny problem, is the specific function of the mental health professional in disability evaluation. It is natural and appropriate for a supervisor to turn to a health service for assistance when an employee is not functioning in his job and when there appears reason to suspect that this may be related to his health. It is generally appreciated that an individual may be ineffective in his work without being emotionally disturbed, but the converse, that someone may be emotionally disturbed and yet remain quite effective in his job does not yet have similar widespread understanding. Mental illness alone does not automatically imply disability. A mental health service should only be called on to do a formal disability evaluation after the judgment has already been made that the employee is disabled, that is, is not functioning satisfactorily on his job, and administrative action will be taken if no health factors are found. Structuring the situation in this manner is advantageous to the employee, since it encourages him to be honest with the psychiatrist. The report of such an evaluation should not be expected to go beyond a statement of the presence or absence of illness, therapeutic recommendations and a description of the nature of the employee's psychiatric problem in functional terms that have meaning to a lay person in the context of the job situation. The limitation of the mental health professional in his knowledge of the individual work situation should be respected and he should not be asked to be more specific than he can be. Rather, it should be the responsibility of the supervisor to use this information in resolving the problem. It is hoped, however, that a supervisor, having a question, will not delay asking for assistance until a formal disability evaluation is requested. A mental health program should permit him to informally ask for and receive consultation without the employee being seen by the service, and to informally suggest that the employee himself seek a confidential consultation.

Once the nature of a proposed company mental health program is decided, its organizational placement must be determined. In considering the locus, it would be foolish to ignore the reality of the competitive situation in an organizational hierarchy. Mental health professionals are no less competitive than anyone else. Introducing them into an already established department, however eagerly they may be welcomed, will surely arouse some concern in other members of the department who may perceive them as moving onto their turf. This can, if not carefully handled, result in unfortunate restrictions being imposed on the activities of a program, limiting its usefulness to the organization. The problem is naturally more severe with a full-time person than it is with a part-time person.

Recall that the three general patterns of placement observed in operating programs are in the medical department, the personnel department, or as an independent unit, reporting to a senior executive. To some extent, the arrangement chosen will be influenced by the desired function of the service. Where its primary concern is to be the evaluation and management of the seriously disturbed employee, then it naturally belongs in a medical department. Even where it is anticipated that the activities of the program will be broader in scope, the medical department offers a location of established neutral territory, an advantage to a mental health program. However, it is often only with difficulty, if at all, that nonmedical professionals are accepted as colleagues of equal status in a medical setting.

Where education and training are the major emphases of the program, locating it in a personnel department might be more logical. Furthermore, there is a strong tradition for the employment of psychologists, albeit not necessarily clinicians, in personnel departments and their placement there might be accompanied by a wider acceptance within the department itself. But, when based in a personnel department, acceptance by the employees for consultation or counseling is likely to be more limited because of the involvement of that department in selection and promotion activities.

Functioning as an independent unit within the organization and reporting to one of the senior executives directly might seem to be the best solution, starting as it does with none of the disadvantages of departmental affiliations. This has the handicap, however, of isolating the service from both of the departments with which it must have a working relationship, thus making it more difficult to break down whatever barriers arise as a result of misunderstanding.

It is inevitable that whatever arrangement is chosen, there will be some ruffled feathers in the organization, especially since, in a comprehensive program, the staff will be crossing departmental boundaries more freely than is customary within the organization. To minimize this, the decision about placement must give full consideration to the people who are to be involved and the way they operate, as well as to theoretical factors.

The professional training of the person selected to direct the program (psychiatry, psychology, or social work), will be partially determined by the scope of activities proposed. A program to be concerned entirely with disability evaluation or with the management of severely disturbed employees will naturally require a psychiatrist. One in which the development and administration of tests for job placement is a prerequisite, will likely lead to the hiring of a psychologist. Where a program places high priority on casework and counseling skills with the maintenance of strong ties with a variety of community agencies, then a social worker might be the logical choice. In a comprehensive program, however, these would constitute only component parts. Other activities would call upon skills generally not taught to any single professional group, but likely to be present in one or another mental health professional as a reflection of his own specific interests.

Yet another question is concerned with the use of full-time

or part-time staff. Obviously, for a smaller concern, a part-time person is all that is necessary. Even a large firm may prefer several part-time people to one full-time person, to benefit from the diverse points of view brought by several professionals and perhaps more important, so that the person in this capacity will not be entirely beholden to one corporation for his income. On the other hand, a full-time person is likely to become familiar with the organization more quickly, will get to know it more deeply and is more likely to be trusted in many situations.

Once initiated, gaining acceptance for the mental health program in the organization becomes the central task. Since such programs are not yet customary in industry the problem is magnified. The stigma attached to the mental health professional creates added problems that cannot be ignored. Not only is he often regarded as a witch doctor who can magically divine other people's thoughts and weaknesses, even if he is not attributed the actual power of controlling them, but he is also considered to be a bit peculiar, if not actually crazy, as a result of having spent so much time in association with "crazy" people.

In addition to these specific items that affect the acceptance of the mental health program in industry, there is the general problem of acceptance of any new individual or program. It takes at least two to three years before a mental health program has the degree of acceptance that enables it to be optimally useful.

Maintaining a program once established also requires careful planning, as the remains of not a few apparently solid programs indicate. A comparison between those that have survived and those that have not, suggests that the more successful have been characterized by a broad range of activities, from direct patient service to prevention, that even when they were given considerable freedom and responsibility, they were careful to limit their functioning to a consultative nature, avoiding operating responsibility even when it was offered, and that the program was accepted as company policy from shortly after its inception. Attaching the service to another department, rather than leaving it an autonomous unit, also seems to render it less vulnerable to dissolution.

As might be expected in any relatively uncultivated field, even after the problems of program design and integration into the organization have been overcome, implementation is likely to encounter obstacles. These will most probably develop in connection with staffing the program.

Finding suitable people presents a unique difficulty. In the absence of a defined body of personnel as familiar with the world of work as with mental health, proximity has most often been the determining factor in the choice of whom to hire. Not a few of the older programs were established as a result of the impression of an executive that the professional had something useful to offer the organization. Thus, staffing many of them will be found professionals who have had longstanding friendships with executives, who had originally been consulted by an executive or member of his family about personal difficulties and had been helpful, or who have worked with executives in some community activity. Through these relationships the executive became familiar with the work of the individual and established a place for him in the company.

The situation has not changed substantially over the past years. There have been some training programs established in the field, and their graduates have generally been well received. But the occupational mental health specialist still does not have a professional identity of his own. While a subspecialty of occupational medicine has created a pool of physicians suitable because of their interest and training for industrial medical services, nothing like this has developed in psychiatry. Industrial psychology is an established field, but its emphasis is not clinical, nor is it primarily concerned with mental health. The field of industrial social work is well established in Europe, but not at all in the United States.

SUMMARY

The previous discussion has indicated how the decisions that must be made by a company attempting to systematically initiate a mental health program will be of overwhelming importance in determining the course that program will take, yet the significant elements can be very subtle and indirect in their influence. For this reason, it is often useful to engage a consultant early in the planning stage to help evaluate these factors and enable the company to develop a program that would best meet its needs. Once this has been accomplished, a consultant can also be of help in finding suitable staff for the program.

Such consultation can usually be obtained through groups or individuals, often university-affiliated, active in the field, or through national professional organizations that will refer inquiries to appropriate people. A company that does not wish to go out of its own community for this help can usefully turn to the professional staff of its local community mental health program for consultation and even for part-time staffing. This is likely to be a particularly fruitful source of help, as professionals engaged in community mental health work, which includes occupational mental health, are accustomed to operating within an organizational framework and are concerned with the management of problems in a setting where pressures and demands may be coming from several sources independently, not unlike the corporate situation.

Ultimately however, the choice of a suitable individual must depend on his making sense to the company. A prominent psychiatrist, when asked how an intelligent layman could tell if a psychiatrist was any good, suggested, "Talk to him and see if he makes sense." When asked, "How can you know if he is making sense?" he replied, "You will know."

7 Solutions from the Behavioral Sciences

John A. Myers, Jr.

In the last paper, Dr. Auster clearly differentiated between the clinical approach and the approach of the behavioral scientist. The behavioral scientist, he said, has a primary goal of developing knowledge. And a considerable body of knowledge has been developed by behavioral scientists—principally psychologists and sociologists—studying the work environment. In recent years these studies have led not just to acquisition of knowledge but to the application of research findings in industry. Some of these applications in turn relate to employee mental health. The purpose of John Myers' chapter is to broaden the discussion and appropriately broaden the concepts of mental health to consider recent activities from the behavioral sciences that suggest applications of research findings which may have a positive impact on employee mental health.

As a frame of reference to consider his very large assignment, I asked Dr. Myers: Are there studies that relate job satisfaction, productivity, and morale to mental health or mental disorder? How can studies of work satisfaction contribute to action programs that may positively affect the mental health and motivation of members of a work group? What kinds of research activities should an employer consider to help him understand and develop programs to meet the appropriate occupational needs of members of his work organization? How does a business manager find and appropriately use such professionals in support of the mental health of his employees, members of management, himself?

Dr. Myers is uniquely qualified to respond to these questions. He received his Master's degree in 1945 and his Doctor's degree in 1950 from the State University of Iowa in the field of experimental psychology. Thereafter, he served as head of the Department of Psychology at Willamette University in Salem, Oregon. He then returned to his home town of Topeka, Kansas, to serve as chairman of the Department of Psychology at Washburn University from 1953 to 1958. He has also been a management consultant and a senior vice president of the Capital Federal Savings and Loan Association of Topeka. Completing one phase of a successful career, Dr. Myers went back to school for a postdoctoral year at the University of Michigan under a Carnegie Corporation grant. Following this study, he joined the Foundation for Research on Human Behavior as vice president. He became president of the Foundation in November 1965.

This chapter deals with some proposed solutions to occupational mental health problems from the behavioral sciences. That mental illness is our nation's number one health problem is common knowledge. The cost of occupational mental illness (both in terms of the industrial cost of the enormous waste of human resources as well as the human suffering itself) is staggering! We do not have accurate measures of this cost; yet we do know that the accelerating rate of technological change is effecting changes in industrial work environment that make it imperative for us to find new and better solutions to these problems. Indeed, whether we can learn how to plan intelligently and to effectively manage the complex, changing, man-machine system, which is the modern industrial organization, is one of the challenges of our times. If we do not make significant progress in learning how to do this, to make this system serve human needs rather than the converse, we may see the beginning of breakdown in effectiveness and productivity as we know it. At the same time we will see unparalleled impairment of individual effectiveness and productivity evidenced in systemwide, pervasive occupational mental health problems. This, it appears, is the shape and scope of the occupational mental health problems facing us, and this is the challenge ahead.

There is an emerging use of behavioral science in industry that may suggest a promising new way to find additional solutions to these problems. It is the study of the industrial environment for the purpose of engineering changes in that environment specifically designed to increase both the industrial economic output and individual effectiveness and work satisfactions. From the research of the past ten years, and especially the last five, we have good reason to conclude that these dual goals are not mutually exclusive. We do not always have to choose between the economic goals of the business and the human needs of those who work in the system. It is often possible to maximize both!

This knowledge breakthrough opens up new vistas in industrial management, man-machine system design, and planned organizational change. If we can find better trade-offs between the psychological need satisfactions of the organizational member and his contribution to industrial output, the payoffs will be tremendous. Competition itself will create the necessity for inventing better ways to manage the industrial environment. The economic success and, indeed, the very survival of the industrial organization may be at stake. For this reason it is not difficult to predict that there will be unparalleled changes in industrial management during the next twenty-five years. The nature of these changes will centrally involve a better understanding of the social forces at work in the industrial environment and suggest how this new knowledge can be engineered back into the system to make it more effective. It is this purposive effort to improve industrial environments that may very well turn out to be a fruitful new approach to occupational mental health problems.

BEHAVIORAL SCIENCE UTILIZATION

Since the Second World War there has been a rapid rise in the use of behavioral science in industrial organizations. Much of the earlier application efforts, however, were technique-oriented rather than problem-oriented. Psychological testing, human relations training, and later, morale surveys were three commonly used behavioral science techniques. Too often these technique applications had little systematic impact upon the industrial organization. As a result behavioral science earned, with some justification, the reputation of being impractical, irrelevant, and "soft" toward the hard-headed objectives of the industrial organization.

In addition to the technique orientation, there is another significant feature of the earlier application efforts that contributed to the "impracticality" of behavioral science. Behavioral scientists, quite naturally, preferred to identify industrial problems in which they were interested; these turned out to be the ones to which available techniques could readily be applied, without much regard for other considerations. Thus, for example, it was popular to identify "communication" problems. When they were looked for, they were found to be present, of course. One of the popular solutions was to employ some version of human relations training, and when this was done, the behavioral scientist proceeded to look for communication problems in other organizations, where this training could be applied. In this way the cycle of limited problem identification/limited technique availability/limited technique application was perpetuated, with the result that behavioral science had limited effect upon the industrial organization.

In contrast to the period 1946–56, the development of modern organization theory in the past ten years has contributed greatly to a broader understanding of how organizations function. In my opinion, the major contribution of modern organization theory is to provide much-needed conceptual frameworks for understanding the relationship between all three of the major classes of variables that account for an organization's functioning. Organizational change and improvement is most meaningfully conceived in terms of these classes of variables:[1] the technological—the tools, work flow and procedures; the formal structural—the rational structures of the organization; and the behavioral—the motivational and interpersonal factors. For convenience, this conceptual framework might be called a "total system" approach to understanding organizations, within which there are the technological, structural, and behavioral subsystems.

This total system approach provides a better basis for understanding behavioral science applications than does the simpler technique orientation. Most popular application efforts until recently have ignored the relationships between these three classes of variables and have been limited to only the "interpersonal" aspect of the behavioral subsystem. Two major conclusions follow from the total system approach, as regards organizational change.

1. The behavioral subsystem includes variables that affect the behavior of organizational members. These are not only individual ability, motivational and learning

---

[1] Harold Leavitt, "The Engineering of Human Behavior in Industry," in *Industrial Medicine and Surgery*, December 1964.

variables, but also the environmental conditions that affect behavior.

2. In a particular organization, attempts to change one subsystem through changing the relevant variables within that system are limited by the other two subsystems. There is interdependence between these three subsystems. Thus, as a practical matter, attempts to change behavioral variables by applying behavioral science are limited by the technological and by the structural variables. To disregard these practical limitations is to approach organizational change inefficiently and often in an unduly costly manner.

It appears likely that relatively simple changes in the reward structure, which affect the behavioral subsystem, may yield far greater systematic behavior changes in the organization than that which may be produced by more diffuse efforts to change interpersonal variables. Changing policies and/or procedures in a way to make aspects of the reward system like compensation and promotion more consistent with the organization's and individual's needs is a way of approaching organizational improvement suggested by the total system approach. In this way systemwide changes can be effected rather than minute, piecemeal ones.

A MODEL OF THE BEHAVIORAL SCIENCE UTILIZATION PROCESS

The major problem in the successful utilization of scientific knowledge is how to tailor the application of existing knowledge to the specific situation in order to effect particular changes in the organization. Thus, it is the development phase of the research and development process that is of major concern. The total system approach discussed above is a useful conceptual framework for understanding organizations, but it does not by itself solve the major utilization problem. How to use knowledge and contributions from different specialists and from those who have particular operating management responsibilities in the organization, and how to develop individual company strategies for successful change, are two crucial problems. What is needed is a better understanding of the utilization process itself.

The model presented in Figure 1 is a schematic representation of the utilization process.[2] This model identifies the significant events in the utilization process, which are divided into two phases. It also indicates that there are roles for the operating manager, the industrial researcher and the behavioral scientist and where these roles fit in the process.

The beginning event of successful utilization is with industrial problem identification. The operating manager is the initiator of the problem, and it is his appropriate role to make the initial problem statement.

Problem restatement is the next event. The importance of this event is that the original problem gets restated in broader terms and in such ways as to require new information and knowledge. It is at this input point that a total system approach, for example, is especially useful. This kind of conceptual contribution is appropriate for the industrial researcher; he has both the behavioral knowledge and the familiarity with the particular organization.

The input of new knowledge, new behavioral research, as well as available information about the particular organization, is the next significant event in the process. The behavioral scientist from outside the organization is the appropri-

[2] This model, as well as much of the conceptual framework herein, has evolved from collaboration with Dr. Richard A. Dunnington, manager of Personnel Research, International Business Machines Corporation, and his influence on the writer's thinking is gratefully acknowledged.

ate input for new behavioral knowledge. The importance of this event is a further broadening or "divergence" of the initial problem statement. By this time the original problem has been restated further. It is only when these events occur that the creative collaboration of the operating manager, the industrial researcher, and the behavioral scientist can produce an array of possible problem solutions.

The statement of solution hypotheses is the next event. This is the final event of the "divergence," called the "option-opening" phase. The purpose of divergence is to generate as many alternatives or solution hypotheses as possible. In this respect, the purpose is to open up as many options as possible for the operating manager to solve his initial problem.

The "convergence" phase begins with the "critical evaluation" of the various solution hypotheses. This evaluation requires the continued collaboration of the operating manager, the industrial researcher, and the behavioral scientist. The critical criteria used here are still broad enough to include knowledge about organizations and people based upon a wide variety of behavioral research studies. The next event is feasibility testing, which emphasizes the practicality of particular solution hypotheses in terms of the unique problems and characteristics of the particular organization. This is where the outside behavioral scientist begins to phase out, and the process is carried on primarily with the operating manager and industrial researcher. Feasibility testing is the final event in "convergence" and finishes the practicality testing of the solution hypotheses. By this time the best solution has been adopted by the operating manager.

Program development and program implementation, based upon the best solution hypothesis, may require the collaboration of a number of others in the organization. They should be phased into the process at an appropriate

A MODEL OF THE BEHAVIO

PROCESS:
_____

Problem   Problem   New   Solution
Identification ➡ Restatement ➡ Knowledge ➡ Hypothe:

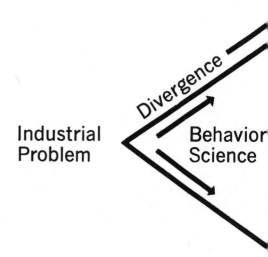

Industrial   Behavior
Problem   Science

PHASES: Option-Opening ⟶ Practicality T

ROLES: Behavior Scientist
         Industrial Researcher
         Operating Manager

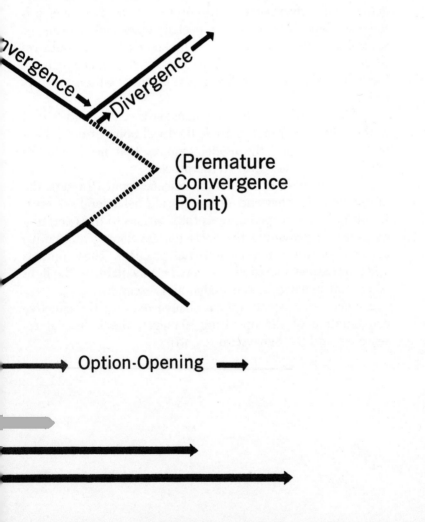

ENCE UTILIZATION PROCESS

.ical   Feasibility   Program   Program
luation → Testing   → Development → Implementation

(Premature
Convergence
Point)

Option-Opening →

time prior to the adoption of the best solution, depending upon their organizational responsibilities. It is they who will be carrying through program implementation, subsequent program evaluation, and therefore later, new problem identification. Thus the utilization process is a continuous and ongoing one.

This model of the utilization process suggests a number of conclusions about successful utilization of behavioral science in the organization:

1. The utilization process is continuous, requiring divergence, and convergence at appropriate times. Divergence is the most difficult to achieve, especially when collaboration of several individuals is required. The knowledge and skills required for successful participation in divergence can be identified and should be developed by those whose roles require it.

2. The role of the operating manager is central and crucial to the utilization process. He is the focal point of the collaborative efforts, and the model requires that he devote the necessary time and effort to the process.

3. The purpose of behavioral science input, through the industrial researcher and/or the outside behavioral scientist, is (ultimately) to open options for solutions to the operating manager by providing the basis for developing alternative approaches to the initial industrial problem. These options and alternatives should be the very best available in the light of present behavioral knowledge and research.

4. Successful organizational change requires the effective collaboration of the operating manager, the industrial researcher, and the behavioral scientist.

BEHAVIORAL RESEARCH FINDINGS ABOUT INDUSTRIAL ORGANIZATIONS

Behavioral research on the industrial environment is yielding findings that lead to a better understanding of the forces at work in that environment. A common feature of much of this research is the information it provides about the needs of the individuals working in the system. Research on creativity and the problem-solving process is one important research area. Another is the survey approach in industrial organizations that yields behavioral data on large numbers of individuals.

There are some useful points of agreement on creativity and problem-solving research findings in the behavioral sciences that we may summarize here.[3]

1. Agreement that the more creative individuals place a greater emphasis on being independent and wanting freedom.

2. General agreement that more creative people are less anxious, are more stable, possess greater ego-strength, and give general evidence of psychological well-being.

3. Some agreement that the less creative are more cautious about their work and more in need of protecting themselves.

4. Some agreement that the less creative enjoy detail work more and get more satisfaction out of carrying out the routine aspects of their work.

5. Some agreement that the less creative value job security very highly and wish to avoid situations where they can be blamed or feel inferior.

6. General agreement that the more creative can tolerate ambiguous situations more easily than the less creative.

Studies providing this kind of results suggest good clues

[3] Joseph H. McPherson, *Creativity: Key to Continuing Progress,* New York, American Management Association Management *Bulletin* No. 4, 1960.

about important human needs. At the same time they begin to suggest new ways of looking at the organizational environment.

Findings summarized by Dr. Joseph McPherson and his colleagues at The Dow Chemical Company relate symptoms of emotional disorder to the problem-solving process in the following ways:[4]

Defensiveness prevents learning new material contrary to old ideas; prevents use of constructive criticism; and leads to too much energy being used to prove oneself right.

Hypochondriasis leads energy away from problems to bodily concerns, and to emphasis upon personal safety and security.

Depression causes a tendency to doubt one's abilities; causes a tendency to minimize findings in reality; leads to lack of enthusiasm; and causes an inability to influence others.

Suspiciousness leads to the tendency to expend too much energy in protection; to having too much pride at the moment to learn; too much preoccupation with status; and too much concern in providing criticism.

Compulsiveness leads to an individual gathering too much information before starting; gathering too much information during the verification phase of problem-solving; the inability to sell an idea because of doubt about his data; and the inability to "hurry" or "incubate" a problem.

There is reasonably good agreement from recent behavioral research on the attributes of the creative person:

1. he has a tolerance for ambiguity
2. he is problem-centered
3. he has a "democratic" character structure
4. he has an unhostile sense of humor

[4] Joseph H. McPherson, *Problems and People* (Midland, Mich.: Ford Press, 1967).

5. he has a high degree of self-acceptance
6. he is independent
7. he is intense
8. he is dedicated.

The industrial organization can improve its economic performance if it can find new and better solutions to problems that range from the discovery of new scientific knowledge to the manufacture the new products. Improving creativity and problem-solving capabilities in the organization is one of the keys to this economic improvement. It becomes good business practice to do so.

Selecting more creative people for the organizational system is one way to improve the creative output of a system; however, this approach must be a supplement to our present approach. Another way is to provide specially designed training in problem-solving skills. This is useful, too, but probably limited unless the industrial climate provides support, nurture, and reinforcement for new ideas and their implementation. The real key to the payoff of enhancing creativity seems to lie in removing the subtle but effective organizational and environmental blocks that prevent better problem-solving. Company policies, the authority and power structure, the degree and kind of task specialization, administrative requirements governing performance appraisal, and even the compensation system, are some of the aspects of the organization that very often impair its more effective and creative output. Add to these elements the rapidly changing technology and what we might call the hidden rules of how to achieve career success in the system, and we begin to see the complexities and possibly conflicting forces that comprise the industrial environment for the individual who works in it. The results may be of the following kind:

1. Individuals' new ideas for improving organizational

output are usually met with any number of the following kinds of "killer phrases" reported by Charles Clark:[5]

> We tried that before.
> Our place is different.
> It costs too much.
> That's beyond our responsibility.
> That's not my job.
> We're all too busy to do that.
> It's too radical a change.
> We don't have the time.
> Not enough help.
> That will make other equipment obsolete.
> We're too small for it.
> Not practical for operating people.
> The men will never buy it.
> The union will scream.
> We've never done it before.
> It's against company policy.
> Runs up our overhead.
> We don't have the authority.
> Let's get back to reality.
> Let's all sleep on it.

2. Management rotation practices, coupled with compensation and promotion practices, usually put a heavy premium on short-term rather than longer term profit considerations. This creates an environment of "playing it safe," "don't rock the boat," and "don't be a trouble-maker." This characterizes the reward and punishment system, and stifles individual and organizational improvement. Defensiveness and suspicion are the rules of the game. Energies are drained off unproductively in playing this game for individual survival.

[5] *How to Chloroform Ideas and Put Men's Minds to Sleep, Creativity Review*, 1, No. 1 (Midland, Mich.: Ford Press, 1955).

Let us turn to the other kind of behavioral research, that which uses survey and questionnaire methods. The survey approach to individual and organizational variables is extensively used in field studies of actual industrial organizations, yielding behavioral data on large numbers of individuals. The professional literature is extensive, and we can do no more here than sample some representative research findings.[6]

1. There is good agreement on findings related to the power and control distribution in the industrial organization. If the formal structure and/or the management system can be changed to increase the influence the organizational member feels he has on the system, work satisfactions and feeling of involvement will be greater.

2. There is good agreement that when this involvement is increased, commitment to the job and motivation to work, is also increased. The result is that both ego satisfactions and ego frustrations are increased, increasing the feeling of risk of job-related failure but also increasing satisfactions from successes.

3. There is good agreement that interpersonal relations are affected by the organizational environment. A coercive, authoritative management system produces more interpersonal tensions, conflict, frustration, and disagreeableness in interpersonal relations than a participative management system. In the latter, there is a greater willingness to see others' points of view and to work more cooperatively with colleagues and more energy is available for job-related efforts.

INDUSTRIAL CHANGE PROGRAMS

Up to now we have looked at some representative research findings from the creativity area and from survey research,

---

[6] Arnold Tannenbaum, *Social Psychology of the Work Organization* (Belmont, Calif.: Wadsworth Publishing Company, 1966).

to see how such knowledge might be useful in planning and implementing industrial change programs. We have a lot to learn about how to use this kind of knowledge for engineering internal development programs. Good beginnings have been made, however, and I should like to describe and comment upon one program I think exemplifies what can be done and what will be done even better in the future.

This was a behavioral research and development project within the General Electric Company. The business problem that stimulated this project was dissatisfaction with the performance appraisal system. It did not seem to be working well either as feedback data the employee could use for performance improvement or as an accurate basis for compensation or promotion.

Extensive research yielded data from those using this management tool for making management decisions and also from those to whom it was being applied. Among other things, the data showed the use of the performance evaluation technique itself had a negative influence on the organizational environment. It did not provide sufficiently task-related performance criteria that a man could use constructively for either effective self-improvement or intelligent development planning. At the same time it was not an accurate enough appraisal of a man's contribution upon which to build the reward system. Finally, it created undesirable and irrelevant barriers between a man and his immediate manager.

The next step in the development process, the evolvement of an improvement program, is difficult to describe because it is highly complex and because we do not yet have a sufficiently good conceptual model of the utilization process. In any case, the researchers, in close collaboration with operating managers, analyzed these data, asked themselves broader questions that the data suggested, looked again at these questions against the behavioral data obtained in the organization, and designed a better approach to get the relevant data into the performance appraisal decisions. The resulting program was called "work planning."

This work planning program was a replacement for the old performance appraisal system. I should like to describe work planning and then make a point of commenting upon the potential such a program has for changing additional aspects of the organizational environment.

Work planning has five simple steps for the manager to follow:[7]

1. Define your own organizational goals and objectives.

2. Communicate them to the employee.

3. Ask the employee to prepare his own work objectives; then negotiate specific individual plans with him, emphasizing his objectives, his plans to reach them, and the due dates or measures to be applied.

4. Review progress with the man on a planned basis.

5. Recycle this continuous process of defining, communicating, negotiating, and reviewing.

The purpose of these steps is to develop a work plan for each individual employee, a plan with individual goals and tasks which will contribute to the organizational goals, and

[7] E. Kay and R. Hastman, *An Evaluation of Work Planning and Goal Setting Discussions,* Management Development and Employee Relations Services (Crotonville, N. Y.: General Electric Company, 1966).

J. W. Blood, "Increasing Management Effectiveness Through Work Planning," in *The Personnel Job in a Changing World,* New York, American Management Association, 1964.

G. A. Bassch, H. H. Meyer, E. Kay, *Performance Appraisal Based on Self Review,* Management Department and Employee Relations Services (Crotonville, N.Y.: General Electric Company, 1965).

E. Kay, J. R. P. French, Jr., and H. H. Meyer, "Split Roles in Performance Appraisal," in *Harvard Business Review,* January-February 1965.

H. H. Meyer, E. Kay, and J. R. P. French, Jr., *A Study of the Performance Appraisal Interview,* Management Development and Employee Relations Services (New York: General Electric Company, 1961).

to do this in such a way as to motivate each individual to meet or exceed his own plan.

Conceptually, work planning is quite simple and straightforward. On the other hand, its adaptation to parts of the organization where the nature of the work, the technology, formal structure, and the skill requirements differ markedly, is in itself a difficult and complex step in the implementation process. We shall bypass the implementation problems here and simply look at the power of the program in terms of how it can make significant changes in the organizational environment.

1. By getting the man importantly involved in the process of task-oriented planning that directly affects his work, his feeling of involvement and therefore commitment and work motivation is increased. He shares in the risks of failure, but he also shares in the ego satisfactions that come from success. Provided he has the skills and capabilities required for the job, these changes alone should provide a constructive challenge for his self-actualizing needs and increase his self-esteem.

2. Structurally, decision-making and especially priority determinations are moved downward in the organizational hierarchy, closer to the locus of the problems. In this way there is a redistribution of power in the system, and this could even lead to changes in the formal structure like a redistribution of responsibility and accountability.

3. At the interpersonal level, there will be a significant increase in the frequency of contacts between the man and his immediate manager. Since the occasion for these contacts is task-oriented and the "negotiating" required by the program necessitates discussions of task in relation to organizational goals, the man will come to have a better understanding of his own task purposes and those of the organization. He will see where his efforts fit into the larger scheme,

and this will probably enhance his self-esteem and sense of contribution.

4. In terms of relevant information for making performance evaluation decisions, the immediate manager will have more and better information upon which to make his judgment.

5. Finally, because more accurate information goes into the performance appraisal decisions, there is a better chance for making the reward system, especially compensation and promotion practices, consistently reinforce the particular behaviors that are desirable for the enterprise, and for this behavior to be understood by all concerned.

INDUSTRIAL CHANGE PROGRAMS AND OCCUPATIONAL MENTAL HEALTH

The economic need to improve industrial output makes it imperative for management to improve continually its understanding of organizational functioning and to utilize behavioral science innovatively in the development of organizational improvement programs. There is an increasing amount of available behavioral knowledge about organizational behavior. Most of it is concerned with the motivations and the needs of members of the organization. There is also an increasing availability of information-getting techniques designed to obtain behavioral data. Recent developments of organizational theory are providing better conceptual bases for understanding the organization as a total system. Finally, current attempts to understand and define the process of use of such data show a promise for new breakthroughs in the development of organizational change programs, with the power to affect the organizational environment on a system-wide basis.

We are seeing the beginnings of broadly conceived industrial change programs develop even now, and we shall see many more in the years immediately ahead. There is no way to prove that these developments will make particular kinds of inroads against occupational mental health problems. It is clear, however, that the realities of organizational life can and will be changed on a systemwide basis, potentially affecting everyone who works in the organization. The direction of these changes will be such as to enhance both the important individual needs for self-actualization, growth, and development, and the economic effectiveness of the business enterprise. As these changes occur, the individuals' self-esteem, sense of contribution, commitment, perception of influence on the system, and work effectiveness will be enhanced. The organizational conditions that may be contributing to occupational mental illness must certainly overlap those variables affecting productivity and work satisfaction. Thus, the current directions of organizational program developments will indirectly affect occupational mental health. Even more promising is the prospect of utilizing new clinical knowledge of occupational mental health in the sophisticated development of organizational change programs to create an industrial environment maximally conducive to individual productivity, work satisfaction, self-actualization, and mental health.

8 The Legal Viewpoint

Philip J. Lesser

On June 8, 1966, the United States Court of Appeals in the District of Columbia, ruling that compensation benefits be awarded to an employee, said in effect that the employer must disprove a causal connection between employment and disability in a case of mental illness related to the job. With this precedent, it is no longer necessary in the District of Columbia for an employee to prove that his mental illness is caused by his work to collect benefits under the District of Columbia Workmen's Compensation Act. A report by Trice and Belasco, "Emotional health and employer responsibility," also suggests a trend of increasing employer responsibility for an employee who develops a psychiatric disorder. Their study concerns both workmen's compensation cases and those at issue between union and management that have come to arbitration. Given this trend, it seemed important to include a chapter summarizing recent legal experience and suggesting future patterns.

Some attorneys do not agree with Philip Lesser's brief that mental disorder arising out of the course of employment is the responsibility of the employer. Others feel that although the trend he discusses is not a ground swell, it is more than a ripple. Certainly there has been no overwhelming number of cases of employer liability for mental illness among employees. But the facts are compelling. We must agree with Mr. Lesser, I think, that it is time the ostrich withdrew its head from the sand. This chapter is designed to help the employer do just that.

Philip J. Lesser is senior partner in the law firm of Lesser and Lesser in Washington, D.C. He was chairman of the Committee on Workmen's Compensation of the Bar Association of the District of Columbia. Formerly he was chief counsel to the director, Bureau of Employees' Compensation, U.S. Department of Labor. He has also been administrator and general counsel, Washington Area Carpenter's Health and Welfare Fund and legal advisor to the Hospital Division, U.S. Public Health Service. In addition, he is an associate editor, Law Journal of the American Trial Lawyers Association.

I asked Mr. Lesser to differentiate between the medical concepts of cause of mental disorder and the legal ones. Whose responsibility is the psychiatric disability of an employee when it prevents him from functioning effectively at work? To what extent has the work environment been held responsible for such disorders? What types of mental illness have been held to arise out of and in the course of employment and therefore been held compensable? What can an employer do in a preventive way to reduce his legal liability while at the same time providing enlightened programs to appropriately assist his disabled employees?

The primary purpose of this chapter is to identify and describe the nature and extent of one broad area of responsibility of employers, created by law, for the mental health of their employees. I also want to show, in general terms, the magnitude of the fiscal burden which that legal responsibility has created. Finally, there are suggestions I would like to propose.

Every state throughout the country requires employers to provide workmen's compensation benefits to their employees. Although most employers obtain workmen's compensation insurance to pay these benefits, the premium costs for such insurance directly reflect the magnitude of the workmen's compensation benefits paid.

With minor exceptions, such as domestic servants or casual employees, all workers are entitled to receive such workmen's compensation benefits, from the highest paid corporation executive down to the lowest paid porter. The laws were originally enacted to provide benefits for disabilities due to accidental injuries (unexpected, fortuitous, traumatic events) occurring during the course of and arising directly out of the employment duties. However, by repeated extension and amplification of the laws in the legislatures, industrial commissions and in the court rooms, such benefits are now generally provided for illness of whatever nature, whether organic or functional, which are caused, precipitated, aggravated, accelerated, or triggered in any way by any condition of the employment or by any aspect of the employment environment.

Unfortunately, industry has taken an "ostrich-in-the-sand" attitude about this fact, hoping that it will not be disturbed by reality. This volume represents an important step in removing our heads from the sand and in taking congnizance of what is now a well-defined area of legal liability and fiscal responsibility of all employers.

Trice and Belasco state the problem succinctly:

> For many years it has been fashionable to debate the question: What, if anything, is the company's social responsibility for the emotional health of its employees? A vociferous band of critics has condemned the Tayloristic division of labor which, they say, has created a society of "industrial robots," "apathetic and non-involved workers," and "maladjusted and immature employees." Technology, as best exemplified by the Detroit assembly line, has been pictured as "blowing out the

candle of life." This concern for the human effects of the rationalization of work has preoccupied the behavioral sciences for many years.

But, while academicians have been boxing with these shadows, there has emerged, quietly and all but unnoticed, an entire complex of public and private law which renders the question moot. Acting through various neutrals, society over the past few years has converted the business organization from a purely short-run profit maximizer into a quasi-social benefit organization, economically responsible for a broad range of emotional and physical impairments of its employees. Social responsibility, whether it ever existed or not, has been replaced by fiscal liability.[1]

Restated in terms of the emotional problems of employees, the workmen's compensation laws now make an employer legally liable for an employee's mental illness, whatever its deep-seated or underlying cause, if it is aggravated, accelerated, precipitated, or triggered to the point of disability or need for medical care by any condition of the employment. This is true regardless of whether the employee himself produced or participated in the production of the conditions of his employment that may have operated as precipitating, aggravating, or accelerating factors. Fault or absence from fault on the part of either the employer or the employee plays absolutely no part whatsoever in determining the liability of the employer for the payment of workmen's compensation benefits or the entitlement of the employee to receive such benefits.

For many years physicians have expressed discontent and criticism with the test of "cause and effect" applied by the courts and compensation commissions in implicating employment factors in workmen's compensation cases. The

[1] Harrison M. Trice and James A. Belasco, "Emotional Health and Employer Responsibility," Bulletin No. 57, New York State School of Industrial and Labor Relations, Cornell, May 1966.

courts and the commissions are not primarily concerned with the etiology of the pathologic condition as is the physician. Under the law the "cause" of a pathologic condition is deemed to be any factor which aggravates, accelerates, precipitates, or triggers such condition, or even renders it symptomatic, as will be evident from some of the cases cited below.

For ease in presentation, I have divided this area of legal liability under workmen's compensation laws into three broad categories. The laws themselves do not make this division.

ORGANIC INJURY PRECIPITATING PSYCHIATRIC DISORDER

The first category I have defined as organic injury resulting in psychiatric disorder. This type of case is not new. For more than a quarter of a century industrial commissions and courts have required employers and their insurance carriers to pay workmen's compensation benefits for the emotional or psychiatric sequellae of traumatic, organic injuries.

Merely for illustrative purposes, I have chosen a few relatively recent cases to show some of the typical situations in this category.

In the case of *Ashland Tree Experts, Inc. v. Smith* (366 SW 2d 152), decided by the Kentucky Court of Appeals in 1963, the employee was a man who had been accustomed to hard manual labor. He suffered a sudden, severe strain while attempting to lift the end of a log over a stump. The employer or its insurer paid compensation to the employee for several months after the injury and he was then discharged from further medical care as having no residual effects of this strain. He continued, however, to complain of pain and disability which, upon examination was found to be solely on a psychosomatic basis. The Commission awarded him compensation for continuing total disability due to a "traumatic neurosis" as a result of the accident and the Court, in a written opinion, sustained the Commission's award against the employer.

In the case of *Kennedy v. Williamsburg County* (131 SE 2d 512), decided by the South Carolina Supreme Court in 1963, the employee was a prison chain gang guard who had been attacked by two prisoners, resulting in lacerations and contusions to his head. After the beating the employee became restless, nervous, and highly agitated, and was eventually committed to a mental institution, where his condition was diagnosed as that of schizophrenia, paranoid type. There was a conflict of medical testimony as to whether there was any casual connection between the beating and the mental disease. All of the lay testimony, however, supported the conclusion that there was a casual connection. The Court held that the evidence was sufficient to sustain the Commission's award to the employee for total disability.

In *Haskett v. National Biscuit Co.* (131 NW 2d 597), decided by the Nebraska Supreme Court in 1964, the Court held that compensation was properly awarded to an employee who developed a neurosis that was casually traced to an injury sustained in the course of employment and that resulted in total permanent disability. The employee, a deliveryman, was struck and knocked to the floor by an overhead metal door in the course of employment. He was paid compensation for temporary disability and medical expenses, but the employer contended that compensation for neurosis causing permanent total disability was improper. The medical testimony was to the effect that the employee was suffering from no orthopedic defect, but that emotional tensions had developed into physical symptoms, caused by the accident in question. There was also evidence that the employee had sustained a previous injury to his shoulder, and that he had undergone psychiatric treatment for anxiety prior to the industrial accident. The Court found that the employee was entitled to compensation benefits for his neurosis and the fact that it preexisted the injury was not a defense, because as the Court stated, when an accident is combined with a preexisting condition to produce disability, compensation must still be awarded.

In *Cammeron v. Industrial Commission of Arizona* (405 P. 2d 802), decided by the Arizona Supreme Court in 1965, the Court held that an employee was improperly denied compensation for his mental disease which he alleged was caused by his employment. The employee had received an injury to his back in an accident in the course of employment. He failed to respond to medical treatment and underwent a psychiatric examination. Two medical experts testified that the employee's disability was of a psychiatric nature which was not identified in the Court's written opinion. The Court found that neurosis, causally connected with a physical injury received by an employee, was compensable. The findings of the Commission were reversed and the case was remanded to the Commission with instructions to award compensation benefits.

In the more dramatic case of *Franzoni v. Loew's Theatre & Realty Corp.*, decided by the New York Supreme Court, Appellate Division (Third Judicial Department. No. 8387) on January 4, 1966, an award of death benefits was granted on the grounds that there was evidence of a causal relationship between the employee's suicide and the industrial accidents which the employee had sustained in the course of his employment. The employee, who had suffered several accidental injuries, had developed a psychosis that caused him to commit suicide. There were conflicting expert opinions that the employee did not suffer from a psychosis but that he was merely depressed. The Court upheld the findings of the Board that the accidents were a contributing cause of the employee's mental condition at the time of the suicide and that, therefore, the widow of the deceased employee was entitled to compensation under the New York Workmen's Compensation Act.

The Minnesota Supreme Court upheld an award of compensation benefits for permanent total disability due to a "conversion hysteria with depression" following a series of minor employment accidents and the later refusal of the employer to rehire the employee after he had recovered from the last such accident (*Haverland v. Twin City Milk Producers Association,* 142 NW 2d 274, Minnesota, April 7, 1966).

In Illinois, the Supreme Court of that state held that compensation for permanent total disability was properly awarded to an employee for a traumatic neurosis following the amputation of two toes in a work accident. The Commission found that the employee was permanently unfit for any gainful employment as a result of his neurosis and the Court upheld that finding. In this case the evidence brought out that the employee had previously been given a medical discharge from the Armed Forces after World War II due to a "nervous condition" (*Thomas J. Douglass & Co. v. Industrial Commission,* Illinois Supreme Court. No. 39,557, May 23, 1966).

And in *Jensen v. United Perlite Corp.,* (415 P 2d 356), decided by the New Mexico Supreme Court on June 13, 1966, the Court held that an employee was properly awarded compensation for permanent and total disability as a result of an injury arising out of the course of his employment even though the physical injury had mended and the only explanation for the present disability was psychological and mental. The employee had fractured his arm when he attempted to free a conveyor belt. Although he wore a cast for about four months, he was able to return to work three and one-half weeks after the accident and served in a supervisory capacity for six months. Aside from the arm injury, the trial court also found that since the accident the employee had suffered from headaches, lack of energy, and a depressed state. On the other hand, the court found that the arm had mended well, that there was no nerve damage to the arm, and that the only explanation for the present condition of disability was psychological. The employer argued that the only compensable injujry was the loss of use of the injured arm and that there was insufficient evidence to support a finding of total and permanent disability. The Court concluded that even if the disability was the result of the mental state of the employee and that, physically, the arm was mended, the trial court did not err in awarding compensation for total disability.

As indicated above, these cases are mere samples of the thousands of cases decided each year by the courts and industrial accident commissions in which employers are held legally responsible for providing workmen's compensation benefits to those employees for mental illnesses following industrial accidents.

EMOTIONAL STRESS PRODUCING PHYSICAL DISABILITY

The second category I define as emotional stress resulting in organic disability. This type of case also is not new. Industrial commissions and courts have recognized this kind of situation for many years and have held physical disabilities resulting from occupational stress to be compensable.

The most frequent kinds of cases in this category are those where a heart attack or a stroke occurs following an emotionally stressful episode at work.

For example, in the District of Columbia, the Commissioner held the death of a union business agent to be compensable, where the agent who was an employee of the union, suffered a fatal brain hemorrhage while engaged in a heated argument at a union meeting, defending himself against severe, ridiculing criticism of union officers for the manner in which he had been handling a jurisdictional dispute with another union. The Commissioner held that the strain and tension resulting from the heated argument and the ridiculing criticism so elevated the blood pressure of the employee as to cause a rupture of an aneurism in his brain and produce his fatal hemorrhage (*Vieau v. Carpenter's District Council,* Bureau of Employees' Compensation, U.S. Dept. of Labor. No. 1340-2F. July 2, 1958).

And in *Insurance Department of Mississippi v. Dinsmore* (102 So. 2d 291), the Mississippi Supreme Court held that a state deputy insurance commissioner was properly awarded compensation for disability occasioned by a stroke where the medical evidence was sufficient to sustain the finding that the emotional strain and exertion of the employment was causally connected with the stroke. The insurance carrier contended that the claimant did not suffer an accidental injury within the purview of the compensation act. The court ruled that while disability or death from the physical or medical standpoint must arise out of the employment as a proximate result, it is sufficient, as a basis for compensation, that the work is a contributing cause. It need not be the sole or even the primary cause of resulting disability or death, but if substantial contributing causal connection is found, the claim is fully compensable without apportionment or deduction. The Court concluded that it seems unthinkable, if hypertension may be aggravated either by physical or mental exertion, courts should be willing to accept the physical as causative, but reject, as not accidental, a disability resulting from mental and emotional exertion.

In *Albarella v. Glick Development, Inc.* (244 NYS 2d 107), the New York Supreme Court, Appellate Division, held that the dependent wife of a deceased watchman was properly awarded death benefits where the evidence sustained the finding that the emotional stress and strain caused by two suspicious men loitering around the premises caused the heart attack that resulted in the employee's death. The fact, as urged by the employer, that other watchmen by the very nature of their work are apprehensive about possible foul play was not dispositive in this case.

The highly publicized case of *Klimas v. Trans-Caribbean Airways, Inc.* (207 NYS 2d 72, 1961), involved the claim of the widow of one of the executive officers of that airline for his death due to a heart attack which the Court held was due to the severe emotional strain to which the employee was subjected in connection with his employment.

The deceased was in charge of maintenance of the employer's airplanes. Corrosion had developed on a wing of one of the planes and the president of the airlines became disturbed at the incident and, in apparent reference to the decedent, said that he did not like amateurs working for him. Decedent made several trips to Texas to check on the repairs being done to the plane, which were being unduly delayed because of the absence of necessary repair parts which the deceased, after numerous, frustrating attempts, was finally able to obtain from diverse sources throughout the country. After weeks of harried frustration in getting the repair work completed under the repeated harassment of other company officials, he got the plane back into service. When presented with a repair bill of $266,000, he engaged in vigorous negotiations for reduction of the bill under threat by the president of the company of being fired because the bill was exorbitant. At this point, he developed the symptoms of his fatal heart attack. In this case the Court particularly noted that undue anxiety, strain, and mental stress from work were frequently more devastating than a mere physical injury.

The law reports are so replete with cases of this kind that it would be redundant to review any more here.

PSYCHIATRIC DISORDER RESULTING FROM EMOTIONAL STRESS

The law is now well established that a psychiatric disorder is compensable when it results from an organic injury. It is also well established that an organic disability is compensable when it results from emotional stress. It therefore should not have been unexpected that the law would finally recognize that a psychiatric disorder is compensable when it results from an emotional stress, that is, when mental illness results solely from mental stress without the incidence of any organic element. Although attorneys conversant with this field of law had been expecting this development for some time as a necessary concomitant of the two prior categories of compensability, the final enunciation of this principle by the courts a few years ago was met with much surprise in industry.

The case of *Carter v. General Motors* (106 NW 2d 105), decided in 1960 by the Michigan Supreme Court, has received wide publicity but there have been others before and after the *Carter* case that enunciate the same doctrine. *Carter* is not unique.

In the *Carter* case, an assembly-line employee was awarded compensation benefits for "traumatic neurosis, traumatic psychosis, functional disability and sequella thereof," which were attributed to the accumulation of the emotional pressures resulting from his supervisor's criticism coupled with his inability to perform his job correctly. In this case there was no element of organic injury or organic disability. The disability was solely psychiatric and the cause was solely emotional. The Court held that the employer was legally responsible for providing workmen's compensation benefits to the employee in that situation.

Of less notoriety but of equal importance is the much earlier case of *Robinson v. Bradshaw* (206 F 2d 435), decided by the United States Court of Appeals in the District of Columbia in 1953. The facts are quite dramatic and the unusual result of the employee's mental derangement most unfortunate. Robinson was a truck driver for an employer whose business location was in Washington, D.C. He was sent on a long trip into North Carolina with instructions to return to Washington, D.C., as soon as possible. On his return and after sixteen hours of driving, his truck broke down in the middle of the night in Wakefield, Virginia, a small town with no repair facilities approximately 100 miles from Washington. When he telephoned his employer that he could not make it back to Washington that night he was greeted with a storm of verbal abuse and threats of being fired. About an hour later he started running through the town screaming and yelling that a mob was after him. He was apprehended and, because he was completely disoriented, and no other place was available, he was put in jail. The following morning he was examined by a physician who concluded that he was suffering from acute paranoia with hallucinations and the physician recommended immediate hospitalization in a mental institution. While awaiting transfer to the mental institution, he attempted to escape from jail, assaulted a police officer and, in the ensuing altercation, was shot to death. The Court, in awarding compensation benefits to the widow, held that the employee's death resulted from a chain of circumstances traceable directly to the employee's work. The Court held that the emotional frustration resulting from Robinson's inability to get his truck back to Washington, the criticism of his employer, and the threat of being fired, together with his fatigue after his extended period of driving, all so aggravated an apparently underlying paranoid tendency as to result in his mental derangement, which, in turn, was the reason for his incarceration, the reason for his attempted escape, and the reason for his death. If Robinson had not been shot and killed, it is obvious that his employer would nevertheless have been held liable for his mental illness.

Less dramatic but perhaps of even greater importance is the case of *McMillan v. Western Pacific Railroad Co.* (357 P 2d 449), in which the California Supreme Court held the employer liable for a nervous breakdown sustained by a train dispatcher because of allegedly emotional stresses and tensions which he experienced in operating the central traffic control system of the railroad while "people were shouting at him over loud speakers." The Court held that the remedial and humanitarian purposes of the compensation law should not thwarted by restricting the term "injuries" to mean only bodily (organic) injuries.

In an excellent article in the *Journal of the American Medical Association* for August 2, 1965, entitled "Workmen's Compensation for Psychiatric Disorders," the authors state that informal evidence indicates that compensation has been awarded in many similar cases that are not published in the legal reports because they were not appealed and therefore there was no occasion for the courts to enter written opinions.[2] Observations in my own practice in this field also suggest this is the case.

---

[2] N. Q. Brill and J. F. Glass, "Workmen's Compensation for Psychiatric Disorders," *Journal of the American Medical Association,* 193, No. 5 (August 2, 1965): 345-348.

Typical of the medical rationale in these cases is the testimony of the attending psychiatrist in the *Carter* case as follows:

> We frequently see a situation of this type where the person feels himself trapped in a situation that has no solution, at least to them, precipitating a breakdown, and I think the indications are that this is what occurred here. I think that he has had the personality predisposition towards the development of this illness for a number of years. This is what usually happens, but then this is the straw that breaks the camel's back and they develop reaction (mental illness).

As indicated above, the courts and commissions rely upon the "straw-that-breaks-the-camel's-back" theory to provide the legal basis for compensability in these cases. However, the tenuous threads of causation spun by that theory are stretched even further by a new procedural device adopted by the courts in the adjudication of workmen's compensation cases.

PRESUMED EMPLOYER RESPONSIBILITY

In the past few years the courts have begun to construe workmen's compensation laws in such a manner as to relieve the employee of the burden of proving *any* causal connection between his employment and his disability, where the disability occurred on the job. In such situations, the courts will now presume that the disability is employment related unless substantial evidence is provided by the employer to the contrary. Thus, in the very recent case of *Butler v. District Parking Management Company,* decided on June 8, 1966, by the U.S. Court of Appeals in the District of Columbia, in directing that compensation benefits be awarded to the employee, the Court stated the facts and the law as follows:

After 20 years of employment as a parking lot attendant, . . . appellant became ill during his working hours and did not report for work the following day and ensuing days. His claim is that the employment caused a mental breakdown, and it is not disputed that he was found to suffer schizophrenic reaction.

Section 20 of the . . . Compensation Act . . . provides:
> In any proceeding for the
> enforcement of a claim for
> compensation under this act
> it shall be presumed, in the
> absence of substantial evidence
> to the contrary . . . that the
> claim comes within the provisions
> of this Act . . .

This provision places the burden on the employer to go forward with evidence to meet the presumption that injury or illness occurring during employment was caused by that employment. . . . The employer offered no substantial evidence that appellant's injury was not work-related and hence has not met the burden imposed by the statute . . ."

Most workmen's compensation statutes contain provisions similar to Section 20 of the District of Columbia Workmen's Compensation Act, and it is not unreasonable to assume that in the near future the practice will be universal to require the employer to *disprove* causal connection between employment and disability in mental illness cases, rather than for the employee to *prove* that such causal connection exists. Since the proof of the negative of any issue is frequently impossible, the magnitude of the employer's potential liability looms even greater than in the past.

COSTS

At present, industry throughout the country pays approximately 2.5 billion dollars each year for workmen's compensation premiums and the costs of such premiums are rising sharply. Obviously, the largest single factor responsible for such rising costs is the increase in workmen's compensation benefits provided to employees.

Under the laws of most of the states there is no ceiling on the amount of medical expenses to which an employee is entitled once the liability for his medical condition has been ascribed to his employment. Under many state laws there is no maximum time limitation for the payment of weekly indemnity benefits to a disabled employee if he is totally disabled. In every state the maximum amount of each weekly payment, which is geared to a percentage of the employee's wages at the time of his injury, is growing rapidly. For example, under the Longshoremen's and Harbor Workers' Compensation Act there is no maximum ceiling limitation on the obligation of the employer to pay for the medical expenses of a disabled employee; there is no maximum time limitation for the payment of weekly indemnity benefits to an employee who is totally disabled; the present maximum rate of such weekly indemnity benefits (exclusive of all medical payments) is $70 per week, and legislation is now pending that would *more than double* the amount of indemnity benefit.

Thus, under the Longshoremen's Act and under the existing statutes in many states it is entirely possible for the employer's obligation to amount to hundreds of thousands of dollars to a single employee for medical expenses, hospital expenses, and weekly indemnity payments if he should become totally and permanently disabled as a result of mental illness whose incidence is related in some way to his employment. Even a relatively short-term mental illness can result in the expenditure of thousands of dollars per employee for medical expenses, hospital expenses, and weekly indemnity payments.

These costs will be reflected in higher insurance premiums

for industry throughout the country. More important, however, to the pocketbook of many large employers is the fact that these costs will be borne directly by them since their insurance premiums are determined on a so-called "retrospective basis," which relates the premium cost directly to the amount of workmen's compensation benefits paid by their insurance carriers on their behalf during the prior year.

Tersely stated and summarized, the problem is that of the financial liability of employers for the mental health of their employees. This liability is growing rapidly under the laws of all the states each year. It is most unrealistic to assume that this problem can be solved by changing the laws or their administration. Legislative and judicial trends have been leading further toward disability coverage in other fields such as social security disability benefits and disability compensation laws, as well as in the field of workmen's compensation. The massive trend is toward greater coverage, not reduced coverage.

Rather than futilely attempt to turn back the clock, or to adopt an ostrich-in-the-sand attitude, industry must attempt to cope with this problem as it actually exists. It has been fashionable among many spokesmen for industry to protest the advent of these rapidly expanding legal responsibilities. But protestations merely delay their acceptance, and delay the adoption of constructive and thrifty means to fulfill them.

RECOMMENDATIONS

I suggest that the solution lies (1) in full recognition and acceptance by industry of its financial and legal responsibilities for the emotional health of its employees, and (2) in taking all necessary steps to minimize the incidence, duration, and severity of occupational mental illness.

Specifically, I propose the following three measures: the first is that we radically change our fundamental employment concepts. Industry has generally thought solely in terms of the physical and intellectual skills of the person hired to fill a specific job. Jobs, however, pose not only physical and intellectual demands, they also pose emotional and temperamental demands on employees. Jobs not only pay monetary wages and fringe benefits, they also offer emotional satisfactions that vary among individuals depending upon their personality structures and their specific emotional needs.

The recognition and evaluation of the emotional needs and problems of an individual may play as important a role in hiring him for a specific job as the evaluation of his physical and intellectual skills. A more sophisticated attempt must be made to match the job and the worker in terms of the total dimensions of each.

It should be fairly obvious that matching vulnerable personalities with difficult job situations can readily lead to the types of breakdowns that were found compensable in the *Klimas, Robinson, McMillan,* and *Carter* cases. Certainly it is obvious that an employer would be inviting a compensation claim if he hired an employee with a weak back to do work involving heavy lifting. By the same token, it should be obvious that he would also be inviting a claim if he hired an employee who is incapable of emotionally riding with the punch to do a job involving emotionally stressful pressures.

I suggest the broadening of man-and-job analyses in order to minimize the incidence of occupational mental illness. These analyses should not only be undertaken at the time of hiring of the employee, but they should also be conducted on a continuously on-going basis for all employees.

Secondly, I suggest that industrial physicians be encouraged to search for and recognize the functional elements in an injured employee's disability. In my own practice in this field, I have noted ruefully that most industrial physicians, on the mistaken assumption that industry has no responsibility for the emotional health of employees, refuse to recognize the need of an employee for psychiatric consultation or care following an organic injury. Frequently, they will dismiss the patient from all medical care with words to the effect that "the problem is all in your head," which unfortunately has the effect of reinforcing the functional disability in many cases. It is most important for physicians who practice industrial medicine to recognize that the employer's responsibility for the functional elements of an employee's disability also spells out the extent of their own medical responsibility when they undertake to examine and treat the employee on behalf of the employer. It is important for such physicians to be educated and encouraged to search for the early signs of functional problems following trauma and then to adopt medical measures designed to cope with such problems, including psychiatric consultations or referrals of the patient as may be appropriate.

And finally, it is important that psychiatrists themselves be encouraged to devote more of their practice to industrial psychiatry so that their skills are made more readily available for the alleviation of mental illness in this field.

9 Mental Health and Occupational Medicine

David H. Goldstein

Medical departments in work organizations are the primary re-sponsibility of the thousands of full- and part-time industrial physicians. How does the physician in industry function when a mental health problem is referred to him? What is the medical department's role in psychiatric disability and rehabilitation? To what extent have rehabilitation programs been successful? How can the industrial nurse contribute to the mental health of her organization? These questions were put to David Goldstein who is associate director of the Institute of Environmental Medicine and a professor at New York University Medical Center. He is also medical director of The New York Times.

With one foot in the academic community and the other firmly placed in an industrial medical department, Dr. Goldstein has an excellent perspective from which to answer these questions. But this was not the only reason I asked him to prepare this chapter. Although his principal research interests emphasize toxicology and environmental health, his interest in the individual as a per-son in the work environment has always been apparent. His con-cern for the mental health of employees at The New York Times *led to the establishment of a psychiatric consultant in the medical department some years ago. His educational programs for physi-cians and nurses at New York University have invariably in-cluded a heavy concentration of mental health topics. Those of us who have, through the years, taught for him in this field have been impressed by the depth of his grasp of the application of psychiatric principles in occupational medicine. He was one of the founding directors of the Center for Occupational Mental Health. A specialist in both internal medicine and occupational medicine, he is also president-elect of the Industrial Medical As-sociation.*

The physician in industry has many responsibilities; not the least of these is the role he plays in the handling of mental health problems. In this role the identification of the mental health problems is by no means a simple task. It is indeed rare to encounter an employee who presents himself to the physician with the statement, "I have a mental illness." Many employees with mental disorders continue at their jobs even though some function well below par and may be disruptive to departmental activity. How then does one detect early stages of mental illness among workers? There are many approaches, the more important of which are the following: referral by the supervisor who has observed change in be-havior; observations made in the course of evaluating em-ployees coming to the medical department with a variety of apparently unrelated complaints; through the review of sickness-absence records; referral by the nurse; and although far too infrequent, referral by a union representative.

Most companies, sufficiently enlightened to have an in-plant medical department, usually have a training program for supervisors. It is essential that the physician in industry participate in this activity. It is the supervisor who has the best opportunity to observe closely the behavior of fellow employees working under him. Supervisors should be taught to look for changes in behavior and personality as well as for changes in work performance. It is a wise practice to have the supervisor refer an employee exhibiting such changes to the medical department before considering disciplinary action for performance deterioration. Such referrals have had a high yield in uncovering mental illness in early stages.

If a medical department has properly established the principle of confidentiality of medical information and has really served the employees well, they will present their health problems to the industrial physician or nurse. While many complaints will stem from organic disease, a large number, perhaps a majority, will reflect emotional disturbance. Depression, for example, most often masks itself under the veil of somatic symptoms. Insomnia associated with loss of appetite and weight loss are often immediate clues to the existence of a depression, previously unrecognized.

Modern occupational health nursing has emphasized the importance of acquiring skills in interviewing. With the premium on physician time, the nurse will increasingly be required to function as the first line of medical defense. In the average plant, employees are seen many times more often by the nurse than by the physician. It is obvious then that she must be trained to recognize mental illness.

Another source of detection derives from a careful evaluation of sickness-absence experience; such a review, for example, often provides the first clue to the existence of chronic alcoholism.

Union representatives in the company have the opportunity to recognize or suspect mental illness and to make a referral to the medical department. This will occur only where the union has confidence in the medical department and the objectivity of its doctors. There is a widespread fear among unions that medical departments in industry, and especially those with psychiatric services, operate in conflict with the best interest of the union. There is concern that ventilation in the medical department with its release of hostility will dilute the grievance procedure. Most unions regard medical departments as an arm of management. In reality most exist to serve the patient.

The family physician of course plays an important role in the detection of mental illness. The first company knowledge of psychiatric disability may be when the disability certificate documenting an absence is received by the medical department. Hospitals and other community agencies play an equally important role in the detection of mental illness. Unfortunately such detection often identifies well-established or moderately advanced psychiatric disorder.

Let us assume that a diagnosis of mental illness has been made by one of the doctors on the medical department staff. There follows the responsibility for evaluating the gravity of the illness, the need for treatment, and the disposition of the case.

We come now to the really crucial point in this discussion. How does the physician in industry function when a mental health problem is referred to him? And as a corollary to this, what is the medical department's role in handling psychiatric disability and rehabilitation? It is evident that the procedures that will be followed will depend in part on the psychiatric training and expertise of the physician and on whether or not he has a consulting psychiatrist on call or on his own staff.

AT THE NEW YORK TIMES

For the past five years the medical department of *The New York Times* has been fortunate in having the part-time services of a psychiatrist. He spends one-half day a week in the medical department, administratively responsible to the medical director but, in essence, functioning autonomously. Under such an arrangement all mental health problems are funneled to him for evaluation and recommendations. In addition he is responsible for decisions relative to return to work following an absence due to mental illness, and for guidance in job adjustment and rehabilitation. A private psychiatrist serving as a consultant in his own office could function in a similar manner, but not nearly as effectively. Among the responsibilities of the staff psychiatrist is to know the job requirements, the work climate, the supervisors, and the company philosophy and policy. Additionally, he needs to know the contractural obligations with the union or unions and union attitudes. It is highly desirable that he function in a neutral ground between management and the unions. It is equally important that he maintain communication with the family physician and the treating psychiatrist, be he a private practitioner or in a hospital. He should also have an intimate familiarity with local community resources in mental health.

The procedure to be followed in a typical case is as follows: an employee is referred to the staff psychiatrist by any of the avenues mentioned above. Let us assume that a presumptive diagnosis of a psychosis is made and that our psychiatrist feels that hospitalization and treatment are indicated. He then communicates with the family physician and after the family physician has had an opportunity to see his patient, a treatment program is worked out jointly with the family physician and/or the treating psychiatrist and our psychiatrist. Communication is maintained during the course of hospitalization between our psychiatrist and the hospital staff. We are advised either in writing or by telephone of the patient's discharge and his approximate date of return to work. The employee is interviewed in the medical department by our psychiatrist after his discharge and before his return to work. An evaluation is made of his fitness to return to his former job or to a job that might be modified to meet his present situation. Where indicated, a "job prescription" conference is held jointly with the staff psychiatrist, the supervisor, and the medical director. On occasion a representative from the union and from the company's industrial relations department may also be called in. Once the employee has returned to work, arrangements are made for periodic follow-up interviews with the staff psychiatrist to determine his progress at work as well as to determine whether after care is being followed, as is often required. In using the term "rehabilitation" in returning a man to work following mental illness we do not mean that the company is running a sheltered workshop. Even though alterations in hours of work or job duties may be required, the convalescent employee must nonetheless be able to function at a job. In the majority of cases this is quite possible. To be sure, there may be relapses, and they do require additional treatment and lost time. One cannot arbitrarily estimate how many relapses make a man unfit for his job. This will always need to be an individual evaluation, and there are times when an employee never recovers sufficiently to be able to resume gainful employment in our company.

NO MEDICAL DEPARTMENT?

The problem of handling psychiatric disability and rehabilitation under an employer without a formal medical program is much more difficult. In a situation where there is not even a nurse in the company, it is usually the lot of the personnel department to manage this problem. It is much more difficult for the personnel man to establish communications either with the family physician, the treating psychiatrist, or the staff of the treating hospital facility. There is usually a reluctance on the part of professionals to transmit medical information to a nonprofessional. This is a real handicap to an earnest personnel director who is trying to do the best he can in a difficult situation. Under these circumstances the convalescent employee so returned to work usually sinks or swims based on only his capacity to perform. To be sure, the personnel director may make a referral of the returning convalescent to a consultant psychiatrist on a fee-for-services basis and seek guidance. But most psychiatrists in private practice are very much patient-oriented and have little comprehension of the problems associated with the work environment. They are naïve in the matter of union rules and company policy and seem frequently to be unaware that management is in business to make a profit.

One might legitimately ask the following question: Given an employer with a formal medical program such as ours, what is the extent of success of rehabilitation to be expected? In rough approximation I would say between 50 and 60 percent of our alcoholics are successfully rehabilitated and about seven out of ten of the psychotics are successfully returned to work. One can expect relapses, of course, in both groups. The group of psychoneurotics makes up the largest segment of the emotionally disturbed, employed population and is the most difficult to evaluate in terms of success of rehabilitation. They are more likely to have frequent short-term absences rather than long periods of disability. It is this group for whom the staff psychiatrist can be most helpful. While in general it is not the responsibility of the staff psychiatrist to become involved in treatment, it is in the area of the psychoneuroses that occasional supportive therapy in the medical department can make the difference between continuous rather than intermittent satisfactory work performance.

THE NURSE

In a survey of occupational health nurses, issued by the United States Public Health Service in 1966, it is reported that 40 percent of the nurses who work in occupational health units work alone. In general they have little medical direction. Only one-fourth of them work with a full-time physician, that is one who is regularly present at the work place thirty-five or more hours a week. One-third of the nurses have no regular physician at all. Almost all of the nurses, however (95 percent), reported that a physician was availiable on call. It is evident then that the success or failure of rehabilitation programs for the emotionally disturbed employee in almost half of the plants in the country which have a medical department falls entirely on the nurse. The outcome will hinge upon the training and perceptivity of that nurse. When one recognizes that 93 percent of the occupational health nurses in the United States are graduates of diploma schools only, and that but 4.3 percent have bachelor's degrees, it is evident that we must lean heavily on postgraduate education for nurses. Certainly, however, a personnel department that has the assistance of a professional registered nurse is in a better position to cope with the problem of the emotionally ill than one without such skilled assistance. Under these circumstances, the use of a psychiatric consultant or the utilization of community resources plus the family physician becomes essential. It may well be that with the development of community mental health centers throughout the country, the nurse working alone may be better able to cope with mental illness in her patients. The problem is complex but not insoluble.

10 Mental Health Education at Work

Alex Sareyan

Alex Sareyan has been executive director of the Mental Health Materials Center, Inc., since its establishment in March 1953. Prior to that time, he was director of public relations and promotion for the National Association for Mental Health and before that in a similar capacity with the National Mental Health Foundation. In the late 1940's, he was responsible for producing thirty-one dramatic radio programs on the subject of mental health and mental illness, heard over the facilities of more than 1500 radio stations in this country and Canada. He was the first coordinator for National Mental Health Week. Since 1953, in his capacity at the Center, he has served in a consultative or managerial capacity developing the publications programs of more than a dozen national health and welfare organizations. No one in this country is better qualified to discuss the use of mental health materials.

As a 1934 graduate of the Wharton School of Finance and Commerce, his initial training was for a business career. His leadership skills have been clearly apparent as he has led the Mental Health Materials Center to its present preeminent position in the field. From the perspective of a former board member of the

Mental Health Materials Center, it has been a pleasure to watch it grow under his able leadership.

Most of us who are professionally involved in the field of occupational mental health feel strongly that educational activities for management, for employees, for industrial physicians, and personnel people is an important part of an industrial mental health program. Films, pamphlets, and books are of vital importance to such activities. I therefore asked Mr. Sareyan how these mental health materials may be used in industry. How can they be best applied in industrial training and management development programs? By personnel people? In medical departments and in industrial dispensaries?

"We'd rather put a pamphlet in our reading rack service that would help a wife learn how to bake a cake than one which might help her cope with the day-to-day emotional needs of her family. It's not that we're against mental health. We just don't want to be accused of meddling in the personal affairs of our employees." That remark, made in 1955 by a responsible official of one of the nation's largest industrial giants, aptly characterized the prevailing mood of industry a short decade ago against becoming directly involved in supporting in-plant mental health education programs.

In the intervening years, leaders in the business community have begun to assume a more enlightened awareness and sense of responsibility toward mental health problems. They have done this by taking active leadership in community efforts to provide better mental health facilities. An increasing number of firms are underwriting the expense of psychiatric treatment for emotionally disabled employees. And there are many lines of evidence suggesting that employers are becoming increasingly sophisticated about the desirability of supporting efforts which tend to improve the emotional climate for employees, not only on the job—but in their own family environment.

People who understand each other are able to function with far more effectiveness than those in situations where such understanding is absent. A supervisor's success in developing an efficient and smoothly functioning team depends as much on his skill in handling people as it does on his proficiency in his work specialty. To handle people skillfully presupposes his sensitivity to the emotional needs of each member of his staff. His understanding of these emotional needs and influences that affect human behavior will more often than not be reflected in the long-range productivity of his department. What has been said of the supervisor can be said with equal if not greater force about the relationship of management to staff at all levels.

Encouraging though the recent trend to bring mental illness and mental health into the open has been, the attitudes of large numbers of people on this subject are still colored by ignorance and myths. The chapters in this volume support and document the thesis that mental health programs do have a relevant function in the business setting. Implementation of these programs can be facilitated if all in the industrial community from top management to the rank and file are enlightened about the nature and scope of mental health and mental illness.

The process of informing and educating people for and about mental health can be conducted in the business or industrial setting in many different ways. Before developing and illustrating some of these procedures, it might be helpful to define what is meant by education *for* mental health and education *about* mental health. Education *for* mental health is the teaching of the dynamics of human behavior with the objective of bringing about better understanding of one's self and others. It encompasses mental health of children and adults, as individuals and as members of a family; problems of specific age groups such as the "middle child," the adolescent, the adult approaching menopause, aging; and human relations in general. Education *about* mental health means the teaching of the facts of mental and emotional disturbances such as mental illness, mental retardation, alcoholism, and delinquency. Informed about the facts pertaining to these problems and the resources available in the community for their treatment, people should be better able to recognize and accept their responsibilities as citizens in coping with them through community facilities and resources.

The degree to which the process of educating for and about mental health is successful depends upon the skill employed in making use of the various tools of communication available for this purpose. The primary objective of this chapter is to suggest how mental health programs fit into a business community, and to offer guidelines in finding the proper materials to support them. Such materials include leaflets, pamphlets, and audio-visual aids.

An educational program must have a number of essential components if it is to be successful. It must be carefully planned. It must be directed to a clearly defined need. Those to whom it is addressed must be motivated to take an active part. The program itself must be skillfully administered. And finally, there must be a continuing assessment.

Dissemination of one or even several pamphlets in a series cannot be considered a mental health education program. A film showing at a noon-day meeting, an occasional lecture by a noted psychiatrist, a one-day conference on mental health and the business community do not meet the criteria for an educational effort that is likely to produce results.

The pamphlet or leaflet, the film or filmstrip, the one-day conference, the seminar or series of seminars, the poster and exhibit must all be considered as *supporting* elements. Each of these methods has its particular merits. And each has very decided limitations in carrying the full brunt of an educational program on its own.

A lecture illustrated with a dramatization on film is apt to present a much more complete picture of a concept or an idea than one that relies exclusively on the ability of the lecturer to communicate to his audience by word of mouth alone. A dramatized or illustrated lecture that concludes with the distribution of a leaflet or pamphlet which reinforces the points made in the presentation becomes a more meaningful educational experience than one that does not. In some instances role-playing as a method of illustrating a principle or a technique will considerably enrich a learning experience. The company newspaper, the personal communication, whether it be written in the form of a letter or verbal as in a counseling situation, will offer major opportunities for mental health education. But again, their educational impact increases in direct ratio to the skill employed in using the various tools of communication in these settings that may be appropriate to the particular situation. For example, the waiting or reception area of a medical office is an ideal place to have a rack displaying leaflets and pamphlets on a variety of health problems. The employee visiting such a unit is motivated by a health problem and receptive to information on health matters. Such a location is a particularly good one for a poster or an exhibit where the impact of its message will be sustained for a longer period of time than if it were located where foot traffic passed by rather quickly. And when the visit with the physician or nurse is ending, a particularly advantageous opportunity occurs for dispensing a leaflet or pamphlet that may serve to reinforce any ideas that may have been made in the diagnostic, counseling, or treatment setting.

FORMULATE YOUR OBJECTIVES

Before initiating a mental health education program, formulate your objectives. Once these are clearly in focus, it will be relatively easy to decide on a course of action and to decide what supporting educational materials will be essential for meeting the program objective. Let us assume that one of your objectives is to help supervisory employees become more sensitive to the particular needs of the employee who is troubled or emotionally upset. In seeking fulfillment of this aim, it is hoped that the troubled employee will be so sympathetically handled that, if this is indicated, a prompt referral to the medical department or counseling service will be made. Understanding of the reasons contributing to emotional disturbances may also contribute to more intelligent placement of the troubled employee in the department. Even more important the purpose of such an educational program might be to assist the supervisor in coping with the perennial problems confronting any management team and arising from absenteeism, accidents, alcoholism, labor turnover, aggravated occupational illness, grievances, and the multitude of other negative responses related to job dissatisfactions.

DEVELOP A PLAN

In planning a mental health education program, once the objectives have been determined, it is important to ascertain which group or groups are to be the focal point of your effort, to determine the methods to be used in achieving the objective, to select the supportive materials to be employed in the program. It is particularly important to devise a plan for a continuing evaluation of the program so as to be alerted to its progress relative to the goal or goals.

An educational program is much more likely to bring about a change in attitude or a course of action in terms of a stated objective if it is focused on a particular group such as the supervisory employees rather than addressed to the rank and file. To put it another way, the narrower and more precise your audience, the easier it is to plan a program that will focus sharply on the needs of that particular group. The broader and more diverse the interests of your audience, the blunter, you can be sure, will be the impact of any educational effort.

The homogeneous audience is easier to motivate than the heterogeneous group. The more highly motivated a group is at the beginning of a program, the easier it is to plan a program that will have the potential for success. The highly motivated audience recognizes a need for gaining information or new insights to improve its ability to cope with common problems with a higher degree of competence. Following are a few examples of mental health education programs directed to homogeneous, highly motivated groups in an industrial setting:

1. A seminar series on "Helping the Troubled Employee" directed to supervisory employees.

2. A documentary film demonstrating job-skill capabilities of the vocationally trained mentally retarded person—directed to employees of departments planning to place mentally retarded employees.

3. Preparation for retirement—directed to employees approaching retirement within twelve months.

4. Psychological first aid—directed to employees with designated responsibilities for handling people in potential disaster situations.

5. Understanding child growth and development—for employees who as parents may be troubled by complexities of child-rearing.

6. Understanding the menopause—directed to employees receiving attention in the plant medical office.

7. Understanding the problem drinker—directed through plant medical office to those employees for whom this is a personal problem and/or to their families.

People are apt to be more highly motivated at the onset of crisis situations than at times when all is well or the pressures of a stressful occurrence or problem have passed. Expectant parents, for example, are much more likely to be receptive to a program on child growth and development than parents whose offspring have reached adolescence (or college age level). The worker facing retirement in a year is much more apt to take seriously an effort designed to help him cope with the diverse personal problems related to cessation of active employment than the worker who is in his forties or fifties.

But it is not enough to reach an audience when it is highly motivated or apt to be in a responsive frame of mind for a particular educational message. A plan must be developed that will be right for the particular audience. Consideration must be given to selecting the methods to be used and determining what materials are to be used to achieve the desired objective. An excellent description of this process appears in the Metropolitan Life Insurance Company's pamphlet, "Health Education in Industry." Although focused on a health program for industry, its strategy and guidelines are highly relevant. This is what the authors have to say on planning a health education program in industry:[1]

In industry two main approaches are available. Individuals can be reached directly on specific problems that concern them personally. Groups of employees can be reached on problems and interests which they have in common. The individual ap-

---

[1] Adapted from *Health Education in Industry* by Melvin M. Udel and Elizabeth Kasey (New York: Metropolitan Life Insurance Company, 1962).

proach and group approach call for different methods. Program objectives also determine the choice of methods and materials used in health education.

Individual approach. Employee conferences and day-to-day contacts with individual employees constitute the most effective part of the individual approach. Opportunities provided through the employee health service are the main avenues for reaching the individual. These specific avenues are the same as those used in making the initial survey. Personal interviewing and counseling provide valuable opportunities for health teaching, especially when the interviewer is sensitive and alert to the wants and needs of employees.

The periodic health examination, for example, often turns up opportunities for individual counseling. An older employee who is overweight may be interested in the relationship between excess poundage and heart disease. Employees who are parents are likely to be particularly interested in information about child rearing. Questions on how to use the employee health benefits program often provide an opening to further discussion.

Group approach. The group approach makes use of a variety of health education methods to effect group change. The effectiveness of the methods chosen depends upon how they fit into the long-range program plans and on the facilities and personnel policies of the company. Group conferences, committee meetings, and employee safety committees provide ready-made but frequently neglected avenues for getting health facts to employees and their group leaders. Many studies have shown that employees are receptive to information from their informal leaders.

The small group meeting limited to employees with some specific interest or special health problem may be a time-saver. Under skilled leadership, group discussions on specific problems—absenteeism, diabetes, or weight control—bring together employees with a common problem, and can be instrumental in bringing about desirable change. Weight reduction programs have been successfully conducted by several large companies, using a combination of individual counseling and the group approach.

Company-wide meetings and informal group discussions are fairly common. The tools most frequently used are such familiar health education materials as:

Posters and Exhibits: These are excellent attention-getters and can be used to reach groups which customarily do not attend employee meetings or read publications. An effective poster or exhibit should have a single message—brief, simple and clearly visible; it should be illustrated simply and vividly; it should have personal appeal; and it should be changed frequently.

Pamphlets: Probably no other tool is more widely used—and sometimes misused—than a leaflet or pamphlet. Pamphlets selected can be made a part of a long-range program. It should be emphasized that pamphlets are merely one tool. Their distribution alone does not, as many seem to think, make a health education program.

Films: The secret of a successful film showing lies in good planning. Here are some essential steps: preview of the film before it is shown; introductory remarks before showing the film to bring out important points to look for; some thought-provoking questions to stimulate discussion; group discussion immediately after the showing, led by a skilled discussion leader.

Employee Publications: Well-written articles, cartoons, and fillers relating to the health education program can be used to reach employees and their families. Here again the messages should be simple and clearly stated, with a personal interest which has meaning for the individual.

PLANNING A MENTAL HEALTH EDUCATION PROGRAM FOR SUPERVISORY EMPLOYEES

At this point, it may be helpful to describe a mental health educational program designed for supervisory employees.

Earlier I referred to a program to aid supervisors in dealing with troubled employees. Such a program is best handled through a series of small group sessions limited to from fifteen to twenty-five persons. The leader should be someone with a high degree of competence in psychological counseling and in discussion technique.

Because it is axiomatic that to understand other people's needs, one must first understand one's own needs and drives, such a series should begin with a program focused on self-understanding. The first session might be introduced by a fifteen-minute animated film, "How Are You?"[2] produced cooperatively by the Medical Services Division of the Minnesota Department of Public Welfare and the Communication and Community Services Division of the Nebraska Psychiatric Institute. In a highly entertaining and informative manner, the film defines normal behavior, discusses mental health and mental illness and then presents some of the ways in which mental illness can manifest itself. It closes with an appeal to the individual to appraise his own mental health. A film such as this could be expected to evoke considerable discussion on the nature of mental health and mental illness. An excellent leaflet, "Mental Health is 1, 2, 3 . . .,"[3] which reinforces many of the ideas presented in the film might be distributed at the end of the session for further reading.

The second session might get underway with a brief review of the contents of the leaflet referred to above. Another brief and excellent animated film produced by the Health and Welfare Division of the Metropolitan Life Insurance Company, *Mr. Finley's Feelings*,[4] might serve as a focal point for the major discussion for this second session. In this

[2] Nebraska Psychiatric Institute, 602 South 44th Avenue, Omaha, Nebraska 68105.

[3] National Association for Mental Health, 10 Columbus Circle, New York, N. Y. 10019.

[4] Association Films, 600 Grand Avenue, Ridgefield, N. J. 07657.

film Mr. Finley reacts to a stressful job situation by committing a rash act. This only brings about more problems and tensions. He doesn't recognize that his emotional reaction to stress stems from his feelings about authority figures. After talking with a friend he begins to realize that his behavior under stress follows a pattern of displacing unpleasant emotions. Once again, a pamphlet might be distributed at the conclusion of this session, also produced by the same firm, entitled *Stress and Your Health*.[5]

The third session might focus more directly on the supervisor's own feelings, thoughts and actions in dealing with others, and how they can affect his relation with those related to him in work situations. An excellent introduction to this presentation is offered in the thirty-five minute film, *The Inner Man Steps Out*,[6] produced by Henry Strauss Productions:

> "The Inner Man Steps Out" tells the story of Jerry Allen, a supervisor who has trouble getting along with others and himself. The audience carefully follows Jerry as, despite his earnest intent to be "decent," his efforts to follow good human relations rules backfire. He is seen in actual problem situations with his family, the men and women he supervises, and with his boss. Animation is used to explain how at least two "inner men" exist inside of everyone—representing each person's need for security and importance. With the help of a third "inner man," Jerry Allen realizes his own lack of understanding of the feelings and inner needs of other people.

The Inner Man presents a rich mine of ideas for a stimulating discussion or series of discussions on human relations at work in the industrial setting. The film is so designed that

[5] Health and Welfare Division, Metropolitan Life Insurance Company, 1 Madison Avenue, New York, N. Y. 10010.

[6] Henry Strauss Productions, Inc., 31 West 53rd Street, New York, N. Y. 10022.

sequences can be selected and used as a basis for extended discussions.

The series might then continue by exploring causes of emotional disturbance on the part of employees. Two additional films which might be used in this context are *Anger at Work* and *Ulcer at work*,[7] both productions of the University of Oklahoma for the Oklahoma Department of Mental Health. It should be noted that for all of the films described, discussion guides are available. These guides which have been carefully prepared and tested before release include many useful suggestions for handling the kinds of questions apt to be raised by an audience. These guides also offer additional bibliographical references.

The series of seminars for supervisory employees might conclude with two or three sessions based on the contents of a pamphlet, "Troubled People on the Job."[8] This publication, prepared by the Committee on Occupational Mental Health of the American Psychiatric Association, might well serve as a basis for a review of the first several sessions. It contains a particularly useful section, "Some techniques for helping emotionally disturbed people," and concludes with guidelines for obtaining help in the community in coping with emotional problems.

Let me close this section on the planning of mental health education programs with a word of caution on the process of selecting the right materials. It should be clearly evident in the particular leaflet, pamphlet, or film that the content is representative of the best current thinking of acknowledged authorities.

Two examples will help illustrate the significance of the criteria noted above. Many pamphlets dealing with interpre-

[7] International Film Bureau, 332 S. Michigan Avenue, Chicago, Illinois 60604.

[8] American Psychiatric Association, 1700 Eighteenth Street N. W., Washington, D. C. 20009.

tations of behavioral problems are currently in circulation through reading-rack programs. More likely than not a glance at the title page of such pamphlets will reveal that the author is not an authority on the subject but a writer who has done a piece for a popular magazine. Such pieces are usually based on a series of interviews with an assortment of authorities. Often these authorities represent a minority point of view within their respective professions. Articles prepared in this manner are rarely if ever reviewed in their entirety prior to publication to be certain that their content is well-balanced and unassailable by a responsible panel of authorities.

Because the particular article is well-written, entertaining, and is on a subject of wide universal appeal, it may be reprinted as a pamphlet and distributed through one or several of the popular reading-rack programs. Such material, though interesting, is usually so superficial or biased in its point of view that the information imparted to the reader serves no useful purpose. Bear in mind that the particular piece was initiated by a writer, however competent he may be. It was he who decided what the article was to be about, and to a large extent was influenced in his decision by what would appeal to an editor. It is true that he may have quoted authorities to substantiate a position. But it was the writer and not the authorities who had the final word about the juxtaposition of the quotes, illustrations, and other data in the piece. Essentially, the end product is a journalistic creation designed to capture public attention. There is nothing wrong with this approach when used in the medium for which it is intended. But it is in sharp contrast to the educational pamphlet which is conceived and developed as an educational tool as will be readily observed from the following illustration. The pamphlet "Troubled People on the Job" was formulated by a group of psychiatrists, all of whom had been intimately involved in providing psychiatric consultation and services to industry. After formulating their ideas and guidelines for such a pamphlet, they secured the services of one of the nation's outstanding mental health educators who also had an impressive background as an author to do the actual writing of the manuscript. This was then reviewed by each member of the committee and finally accepted as representing their best collective judgment on suggestions for helping supervisory employees cope with the problems of troubled employees. The manuscript was then reviewed and accepted for publication by another committee of the American Psychiatric Association, the professional membership association of 16,000 psychiatrists in the United States. A special preface was added to the manuscript by the president of the Association. The forty-page pamphlet that emerged as a result of this effort was over two years in preparation. This does not mean that every acceptable mental health education tool must go through such a lengthy refining process. But if it does, the chances are that when it emerges it will have substance, integrity, validity, and authority, all essential components of a sound mental health education piece.

WHERE TO GO FOR HELP IN PLANNING AN INDUSTRY-ORIENTED MENTAL HEALTH EDUCATION PROGRAM

The National Association for Mental Health through its state divisions and local affiliates is knowledgeable, not only about community mental health resources but also about individuals in their respective communities who because of their professional competence may be used as program consultants. These associations can also offer suggestions for industry related mental health programs and sources for program materials. A list of the state divisions and addresses may be obtained by application to the National Association for Mental Health, 10 Columbus Circle, New York, N. Y. 10019.

Governmental agencies concerned with mental health and health services at the local, county, and state level are another important source for program assistance. The most direct way to locate such resources would be to communicate with either the State Department of Health or the State Department of Mental Health. (In many states, mental health educational activities and services are the responsibility of the health department.) In many instances, the state agency can provide samples of appropriately useful program materials. Practically every state agency also maintains free loan film libraries from which mental health films may be secured.

At the federal level, information concerning program assistance or selective bibliographies and listings of materials appropriate for use in mental health-oriented programs in industry are available from a number of agencies. Among these are the following:

Publications and Reports Branch
National Institute for Mental Health
Barlow Building, 5454 Wisconsin Avenue
Chevy Chase, Md. 20203

National Clearinghouse for Mental Health Information
National Institute for Mental Health
Barlow Building, 5454 Wisconsin Avenue
Chevy Chase, Md. 20203

Children's Bureau
Department of Health, Education and Welfare
Washington, D.C. 20201

Vocational Rehabilitation Administration
Department of Health, Education and Welfare
Washington, D.C. 20201

Administration on Aging
Department of Health, Education and Welfare
Washington, D.C. 20201

A number of voluntary agencies and commercial organizations can serve as an important source of information and guidance on mental health programs in industry. Among these, the Mental Health Materials Center, 104 East 25th Street, New York, N.Y. 10010, provides a unique and particularly helpful service. Through its Human Relations Aids Program Packet Service, this nonprofit organization provides a screening service to persons with responsibility for selecting and planning use of program materials in the field of mental health, family life and human relations. Persons subscribing to this service receive six program packets a year. Each packet contains copies of leaflets, pamphlets, and descriptions of audiovisual aids that have been carefully sifted by its editorial staff and board of consultants. Only those items are commended that meet the rigorous standards established by the Center. The material reviewed in this service covers the gamut from infancy through maturity. Subjects covered range from alcoholism, child development, human relations through mental health in its various forms.

The Mental Health Materials Center is also a source for a number of publications highly appropriate for use in industry related mental health programs. Other agencies with a high repute for educational materials that would be appropriate for use in business settings are:

American Medical Association
535 North Dearborn Street
Chicago, Illinois 60610

Metropolitan Life Insurance Company
1 Madison Avenue
New York, N.Y. 10010

Public Affairs Committee
381 Park Avenue South
New York, N.Y. 10016

Another national agency that not only has publications appropriate for industry use, but program consultation services as well is:

The National Council on Alcoholism
2 East 103rd Street
New York, N.Y. 10029

Selected Mental Health Publications Appropriate for Use in Industrial Settings

"Pierre the Pelican Retirement Series." A series of twelve pamphlets addressed to the man approaching retirement. It attempts to anticipate many of the problems faced by the employee about to retire. There is a strong mental health component running throughout the series. Prepared by Loyd Rowland, Ph.D., and published by The Garden District Educational Services, 1528 Jackson Avenue, New Orleans, Louisiana 70130.

"Blondie." In this comic book, Blondie, Dagwood, and the rest of the Bumstead family teach some basic mental health concepts. Four separate episodes about the family deal with such ideas as: handling angry feelings, showing consideration for others, facing up to responsibilities, and doing things on one's own. Adapted by Margaret Farrar and Joe Musial. Published by New York State Department of Mental Hygiene, Albany, New York.

"Crisis in the Family." The material in this pamphlet is based on research showing that individuals and families can better withstand periods of crisis and emotional stress if they receive the right kind of help at the critical time; that help can be given to the troubled person by relatives and friends as well as professional personnel; that a little help goes a long way, and that the right kind of help will determine to a large extent whether people survive their crisis in a mentally healthy way. Prepared by Vivian Cadden in consultation with Gerald Caplan, M.D. Published by National Research Bureau, Burlington, Iowa.

"Seven Keys to a Happy Life." This pamphlet is a sound dose of "self-understanding" by a recognized authority; a valuable restatement of basic principles; a catalog of ideals to clarify what is meant by "mental health." By William C. Menninger, M.D. Published by National Research Bureau, Burlington, Iowa.

"Your Emotions and Overweight." This pamphlet is the first written for laymen that focuses on underlying emotional factors leading to unhealthy eating patterns and overweight. It provides information on overweight and suggests resources for medical and other professional help in alleviating some of the causes and in establishing healthy eating patterns. It does not prescribe diets. By Elizabeth M. Dach. Published by Mental Health Materials Center, 104 East 25th Street, New York, N.Y. 10010.

"First Aid for Psychological Reactions in Disasters." This is an excellent manual providing practical guidelines for handling psychological casualties in times of unusual stress. Although primarily concerned with psychological problems arising out of disaster situations, it has many useful implications for the handling of emotionally disturbed people. A discussion guide is available—considerably enhancing its value for educational purposes. Prepared by the Committee on Disaster and Civil Defense of the American Psychiatric Association. Published by the American Psychiatric Association, 1700 Eighteenth Street, N.W., Washington, D.C. 20009.

"Understanding Your Menopause." This pamphlet presents the menopause as a natural process that need cause most women little or no distress, rather than as the catastrophe which it may have seemed to their grandmothers. Solid information set forth in a warm and reassuring manner prepares the reader to cope with the adjustments, both emotional and physical, which do inevitably appear. Written by Stella B. Applebaum and Nadina R. Kavinoky, M.D. Published by Public Affairs Committee, 381 Park Avenue South, New York, N.Y. 10016.

"How to Recognize and Handle Abnormal Behavior." Policemen are constantly dealing with people whose conduct is antisocial or abnormal or at least bizarre. Of course the foreman in a plant or the supervisor in an office ordinarily deals with less spectacular "cases"; but the guidelines set forth in this manual for policemen will often help them too. Written by Robert A. Matthews, M.D., and Loyd W. Rowland, Ph.D. Published by National Association for Mental Health, 10 Columbus Circle, New York, N.Y. 10019.

"Children of Working Mothers." Seven and a half million working mothers have children under eighteen—a fact that underlines the importance of adequate care for such children. This booklet suggests ways to increase benefits and minimize disadvantages for children of working mothers, so as to strengthen the mental health and well-being of both. Written by Elizabeth Herzog for the Children's Bureau. Published by U.S. Government Printing Office, Washington, D.C. 20402.

III

The Stress
of the Executive

11 Executive Stress

Graham C. Taylor

To Work Is Human: Mental Health and the Business Community *was prepared primarily for employers. Many who read this book will therefore be managers. Others will be top-level executives. For this reason it seemed worthwhile to broaden the area of our concern to include comment on the mental health of many of our readers, thereby suggesting that our concerns are not limited to the hourly employee; that managers and executives are as susceptible to emotional difficulties as are those they supervise. The following three chapters examine the roles key managers play in coping with an increasingly competitive and complex milieu brought about by rapid technological and administrative advances that affect most phases of their personal and organizational life.*

To introduce the subject, Graham Taylor was asked to define the aspects of the executive's business life that he has observed to be particularly stressful. I asked him: What factors in an organizational subculture appear to produce emotional reactions in executives? Is it true that top management people are more prone to ulcers, hypertension, coronary artery disease, and psychosomatic reactions? Is the ego-involved, responsible manager more reactive to his work situation than others? What are the particular sources of job pressure to which he is apparently reacting? Are there particular personality types who are drawn to responsible management positions and, if so, are there pitfalls such people might consciously identify and avoid? While he failed to answer these questions directly, his response serves well to launch our discussion.

Dr. Taylor considered his topic from the viewpoint of an experienced psychiatric consultant to industry. He is an assistant professor of psychiatry at McGill University in Montreal, Canada. He is also psychiatric consultant for the Aluminum Company of Canada, as well as for other local industries. For some years prior to his present work, he was psychiatric consultant to the Jones and Laughlin Steel Company and on the faculty of the University of Pittsburgh, Graduate School of Public Health. He received his medical degree from McGill University Medical School in 1943 and is a graduate of the Allan Memorial Institute of Psychiatry. From 1948 to 1950, he was a Carnegie Fellow in Industrial Psychiatry at Cornell University. His memberships and fellowships suggest his wide-ranging interests and include the Industrial Medical Association, the American Sociological Association, the Society for Applied Anthropology, the Group for the Advancement of Psychiatry, and the American Psychiatric Association. For many years, he served as a member of the APA Committee on Occupational Psychiatry and is coauthor with me of the book Mental Health in Industry.

As we look back on the last fifty years or so, one wonders not that so much stress for the executive exists but that there is so little. The nature and background of work, its tempo, the work group, the milieu of work, the family, and the neighborhood have all changed extensively. To all these changes the human has constantly had to adjust. Looking back even further, one sees that man has always had to adapt to changing conditions. Man has always worked, but it is unfortunate that things he learned over thousands of years of

adaptation—plowing, building, or perhaps making shoes—
do not now apply.

Man finds himself caught up in a maelstrom. Change
boils, swirls, and seethes about him as he is carried through
the rapids to the age of automation. What lies ahead is
mainly a matter of speculation and there is an unease regarding the things that the cybernetic revolution has
brought and those yet to be revealed. However, this discussion cannot take the space to deal too much with the problems of automation as we look at the executive at work
today. They are, however, important to bear in mind.

To understand some of the stresses the executive feels, we
must first understand something of the nature of work today.
There has been an increasing depersonalization and aliena-
tion of man both from his work and from life itself. In this
way, conditions were not improved by the advent of the
industrial revolution. Work became frustrating, uncreative,
and to a large proportion of the population, only a means of
making a living, a necessary evil. Even at the executive level,
the rationale is, as I pointed out in a recent paper, an unpleasant interlude between weekends.[1] The doctrine that
work has value solely as a utility was assumed by Freud
who, as David Riesman has pointed out, felt that individual-
istic motives of getting on in the world, and desires for fame
and success were perfectly natural. It did not occur to him
that they might be culturally stimulated or produced, let
alone that they might be, in themselves, neurotic drives.
There is today a great need for a *rehumanization* of work so
that it may become what it should be to all of us—a means
to a higher potential in our appointed lot. However, I will
deal with this point later since it is first important to consider the stresses that operate in work today.

[1] "Work and Leisure in the Age of Automation," *Main Currents in
Modern Thought* (May-June 1966) 22:116.

STRESS

Whenever we think of stress, we tend to generalize, secure in an overall view of what stress really is. Often we are not too personally involved and tend to speak in vague terms that soon become platitudinous. These terms serve well as a defensive wall against personal involvement.

We think of stress as something that is harmful or deleterious to performance and, in general, we wish to eliminate it. However, we would do well to note that stress is often accompanied by, and indeed may be a necessary part of, the processes of change and growth. It is a paradox that many of our actions are designed to reduce stress, but consider what would result if we achieved all of our goals and eliminated all of stress. Without some degree of stress, there would be no productivity and almost certainly there would be boredom. When the stress factor is nonexistent, we are dead. When the stress factor is too great, it stifles and finally crushes us.

In the physical world, we may presume that objects react to different stress in a more or less uniform manner. But in the realm of human behavior the situation, complicated because the result of a stress situation, is a function both of the force applied and the particular reaction of the individual. In this way, the executive, whether he likes it or not, is deeply involved in the field of human behavior and of group interaction. In these many-faceted fields, generalizations are indeed difficult, and one can give only a rough map of the territory.

EXECUTIVE STRESS

Without periodic reevaluation there would be no direction to growth. It is with this in mind that the following observations are made with respect to the effects of stress on the executive. One must, however, remain cognizant of the fact that such effects will vary from a stimulus to change to, at the other extreme, an impairment of or loss of function. Indeed, the very matter of diagnosing the stress factors within a company may, at times, be disturbing to the organization as well as to the executive. The identification of a stressful factor itself may create a measure of stress. In direct response to Dr. McLean's questions, I can say here that executives are no more prone to ulcers than others. Indeed, recent studies have shown that it is the first-line supervisor—the foreman—who is more subject to ulcers and other psychosomatic stress disorders. The same may be said for cardiovascular illnesses.

Specifically, executive stress may arise when performance is below prevailing standards set either by others or by the executive himself. In other words, failure to meet external or internal expectations can both be stressful. Obviously, there are a great many potential factors that lead to stress reactions.

First, there is the matter of the work itself. Work overload, long hours, and, related to this, doing things in the wrong priority are often problems. Insecurity, repetition, or monotony are areas too well documented to dwell on, but the sum and substance of it is that most of life's frustration and satisfactions are met on the job.

The executive is involved in decision-making and in the wielding of authority. Functioning in this capacity both in relating to his superiors and to his subordinates may create stress when the authority is involved with personal compulsions rather than with the objective situation. This may lead to feelings of guilt and indecision on the part of the executive and to resentment and misunderstanding among others. Often the executive is faced with the impaired performance of one of the members of his team. He will wonder if this is due to a personal problem and therefore what action he should take, if any.

A major function of the executive is the provision of sound leadership to his staff. There are many problems in this area that can give rise to stress. There is the matter of the individual as opposed to group decisions, and the thorny problems surrounding the manipulation and engineering of consent. The prevailing climate in society tends to be democratic whereas decision-making in industry is often authoritarian. Ambivalences and doubt abound in this regard. These terms are admittedly in the nature of labels, but they do in some way indicate the troublesome setting in which executive leadership may be exercised.

The inevitable isolation of the executive due to his very position in the industrial hierarchy has frequently been scored. This psychological and at times physical isolation and consequent loneliness is, for obvious reasons, a source of stress. There is a danger that the executive may not be adequately informed about the state of the organization. At times, he is carefully groomed and protected, receiving only information about his organization that will fit his frame of reference. Hence, he may feel secure in the false belief that he has a comprehensive grasp of the organization's state.

Our industrial society is obviously highly competitive in nature. The competition among executives is a source of stress: competition for recognition and ultimately for promotion. This is often masked by a facade of harmony and superficial friendliness, which only aggravates the problem by introducing an element of insincerity.

In our rapidly evolving society, changes in values inevitably arise, and these changes will lead to value conflicts. The executive may find himself in conflict with other members of the organization in this matter, or indeed, with the organization itself, viewed as a corporate entity. This may arise when the individual himself has experienced a change in outlook based upon his own inner development as a human being.

We now turn to a triad of factors, all of which can create problems for the executive.

First, the all-important matter of health. Fear of illness and the possible impairment of health can lead to apprehension. This is related to the matter of competition, the fear of being replaced and the fear of impaired performance.

Second, our present society places emphasis upon youth, and the consequent impugning of maturity may give rise to feelings of inadequacy.

This is exaggerated by the galloping pace of automation as it creates an obsolescence of skills, including the skills of decision-making. Probably a good deal of present-day management activity could well be automated out of existence. There is much defensive thinking with people hopefully believing that automation will affect others and leave them exempt.

The third factor is that, for those whose sense of identity has been dependent exclusively on their industrial role, there will be a stress associated, strangely enough, with optimum achievement. Once the mountain has been climbed, there is no further goal to pursue. The absence of challenge can be painful.

LEISURE AS STRESS

The final point I wish to make is not so quickly summarized. It is that a lack of balance between work and leisure is also stressful. Leisure time activity, recreation, and vacations all play an important role in the stress equation. This fact is becoming increasingly important. There is a growing increase in the amount of spare time available to the working man including many executives. We will see the day when conditions will be similar to those found in the ancient Greek society where servants did almost all the work. For this reason we must learn to use leisure in new ways. Not only that, man must learn to look at work in new ways. Work must become self-fulfilling and not self-defeating. It is a reversal of the true order that work for most of us today is a disagreeable five-day interval before the so-called weekend respite. Hence, if automation can free man from an assembly line, it should be welcomed. But, when man is liberated from the necessity of earning a living through dehumanized work, he is at once free to work and live more creatively. As Churchill has said, "Those whose work and pleasures are one, are fortune's favorite children." Many do not seem to know that leisure is not just the presence of free time. To some, leisure seems to be an escape from free time. In the case of the retired, often to be faced with continuing leisure is to be faced with one's own emotional bankruptcy and despair. To others, leisure means frantic do-it-yourself or self-improvement activities.

We can learn from the ancient Greeks who placed true value on leisure—that which makes life worth living. In the time of Socrates, Plato, and Aristotle, leisure meant engaging in something desirable for its own sake—composing and reciting music and poetry, conversation with friends, the exercise of speculative faculties, and the cultivation of the mind. The idea of contemplation was intrinsically bound up for the Greeks with the idea of leisure. Those who could contemplate were considered blessed and happy. Today, a new and perhaps related concept of leisure is required.

We have considered some of the stresses on the present-day executive. Lest it be thought that the picture is totally grim, we may happily recall that one man's stress is invariably another man's stimulus.

12 The Industrial Physician and Executive Stress

Leon J. Warshaw

A born and bred New Yorker, Dr. Leon Warshaw entered the field of occupational medicine initially as an adjunct to his private practice of internal medicine and cardiology. In recent years, however, he has devoted full time to industrial medical activities. Currently, he is medical director of Paramount Pictures Corporation and also medical director of United Artists Corporation. In addition, he has served as a consultant in occupational health to a number of companies in the New York area, the Middle West, and in California. His research activities are also widely varied and include studies in aviation medicine, respiratory physiology, cellular growth and development, and in tissue transplantation. For some twenty years he has been a member of a clinical pharmacology group evaluating new drugs and new methods of treatment primarily in cardiology, and more recently, in psychopharmacology under grants from the National Institute of Mental Health. Currently, Dr. Warshaw is research director of the Industrial Health Research Foundation, Inc., a nonprofit foundation organized to facilitate clinical research in the field of industrial medicine. He is the author or coauthor of some ninety articles in

medical journals and produced two books, the most recent being,
The Heart In Industry. *He serves as associate editor of the* Journal of Occupational Medicine.

*The role of occupational medicine in most large organizations
is crucial to the prevention of disabling stress reactions among
executives. In smaller companies fortunate enough to have good
medical programs, the part-time medical director and medical
consultant play a similar role. It was with the goal of learning
from a medical consultant to many companies, who has served as
consultant to hundreds of executives, that I asked Leon Warshaw
to write this chapter. What can the key manager do when faced
with business pressures that are apparently causing symptoms?
What is the role of the occupational physician? The psychiatrist?
The personnel department? The chief executive officer? Is there a
role for a new group treatment modality where men in key positions can meet on neutral ground to exchange views on their roles
in their individual organizations? Does the annual mental health
evaluation play a part in bolstering the effective functioning of
key executives? These were a few of the questions I asked him to
consider as he developed his material.*

The medical director or the industrial physician who functions as part of a modern comprehensive occupational health
program is, if he is doing his job properly, concerned with
the mental health of the executives in his company. Much of
his time is spent dealing with symptoms reflecting the executive's difficulty in coping with the stresses that beset him
and, even, with preventive measures to help him deal
with problems more effectively and with fewer symptoms.

In addition to his skill as a physician, there are certain
"tools" that such a physician uses to help him do a good job
in this area.

First, and foremost, he requires an intimate knowledge of the industry and the place in it of the company with which he is affiliated. It is said with much truth that each company has its own personality, often reflecting that of the company's founder or top executive. For example, when one knows corporate personalities well, it is rather easy to predict that a given individual would do well with one company but might be a misfit or a complete failure with another company in the same industry.

Further, it is important that the physician be fully aware of exactly what is going on in the company he is serving: What are the problems? How they are being met? Who is doing what and where and when? What problems are being anticipated and how will they in turn be met?

Finally, the industrial physician should know a good deal about the executives of his company: About their physical and mental health, about their patterns of response to specific stresses, about the way they relate to each other, about their families and their off-the-job activities.

It is rarely possible for him to develop this kind of knowledge and information in any systematic organized manner. Instead, it must be developed over a period of time, bit by bit, piece by piece, through contracts with the rank and file employees as well as the company executives themselves. He must have a basic interest in the company and its affairs, a curiosity about people that will impel him to learn to know them, and a warm regard for people as individuals that will earn him their respect and confidence. Above all, he must have the time and leisure for this endeavor. A good deal of this knowledge can be obtained within the medical department itself as individuals come to him with complaints of one kind or another. Much of it, however, can be obtained only by venturing out to meet company executives in their offices, in the executive dining room, and at social gatherings.

One important caution must be observed here: the effective physician is extremely wary of dealing out information instead of receiving it. An innocent remark revealing a bit of information gleaned during a presumably casual conversation may be construed as a breach of confidence. The successful physician exercises great caution in avoiding involvement in interdepartmental politics. He always conducts himself in such a way as to avoid any possible implication that he is so-and-so's "man." Any hint of indiscretion or lack of integrity on his part will dry up his sources of information and impede his attempts to use it constructively.

Against this background, the industrial physician must become acquainted with each individual executive. The periodic health examination is an excellent medium for initiating this relationship. Properly performed, it will include a detailed inquiry as to how the executive is functioning, about the problems confronting him both at home and on the job, and about his plans for dealing with them. Getting the executive to talk about his job as he sees it now and as he sees it developing in the future will often be singularly revealing, particularly if it is at variance with the notions about him advanced by his coworkers and his superiors in the company.

Many emotional difficulties and stresses translate themselves into physical symptoms. These may be purely psychophysiological or they may compound the problems created by an organic illness. The role of emotional stress in causing these symptoms should be recognized, and while therapy for their relief may be proffered, an attempt should also be made to guide the individual to a better understanding and handling of the stressful situations that cause them.

As with executives in Britain, much of the difficulty they

experience stems from inefficient organization of their personal and business lives. They often need instruction in such simple concepts as how to work effectively. This includes developing a capacity to delegate authority to deal with lesser problems—a corollary of this is to make sure that they have sufficient help to whom such delegation may be made. Among other factors that frequently need attention are the need for systematic relaxation, regular vacations of adequate duration and content, and workable itineraries for those whose jobs demand travel.

The industrial physician, to be effective, should spend a significant amount of time with the younger executives, those who are presumably healthy and well adapted to stress. This is the time when proper work habits are best inculcated. This is the time when the conflict arises between demands on the young man's time and energy from the job and the needs of his young wife and growing children for his time, energy, and companionship. This is the time when he must learn to balance his work and his other responsibilities, his play and his community activities, his social life, and his continuing self-education.

While a few personnel directors and industrial relations people have some competence in dealing with problems of this order, most do not. The fact that personnel people do not have the professional mantle that sets the industrial physician apart from line management frequently makes it difficult for executives to come to them. The difficulty is compounded when the executive may have an equal or even high rank within the company structure. A long-forgotten college course in psychology and "just plain common sense" are scarcely adequate tools for handling serious and complicated problems.

It should be recognized that the physician, however skilled he may be in handling personal problems, is usually not trained as a psychiatrist. It is important, therefore, that he have available a competent psychiatrist, preferably one with experience in industrial psychiatry, with whom he may discuss his handling of particular situations and to whom he may refer selected individuals who require psychiatric evaluation and guidance. Also, he must develop and maintain an effective collaboration with each executive's personal physician. The latter is often more familiar with stresses arising in the home or family situation. By pooling their observations and coordinating their recommendations, the two physicians will best serve the needs of the individual in whom they share an interest.

In companies that are too small or too unenlightened to have launched a comprehensive occupational health program in which a competent industrial physician can function along the lines I have indicated, dealing with problems of executive stress is infinitely more difficult. Casual advice from a well-meaning individual who has not made a thorough study of the executive in difficulty and the situation confronting him can frequently compound the problem, even when coming from a person of competence and skill. When it comes from one who does not possess the required competence, the results can be disastrous. When the head of such a company is confronted by this type of problem, he should recognize that it is rarely confined to a single individual although it may be only that individual and his problem that has come into the limelight. He should seek the services of a competent occupational health consultant with whom the problem may be discussed. Often, after surprisingly little investigation, such a consultant may be able to point out other problems and guide the company in developing a program for dealing with them.

Its manpower, particularly its skilled and executive personnel, is frequently called a company's most irreplaceable asset. Enlightened management will institute a program of preventive maintenance to keep it functioning with optimal efficiency. Attention to mental health problems and particularly to their prevention is a fundamental element in such a program.

13 Executive Stress in Great Britain

H. Beric Wright

H. Beric Wright, M.B., B.S. (Lond), F.R.C.S., qualified in medicine in 1941 at University College Hospital in London. He spent the next five years in the Army Medical Corps and was, upon his return to peacetime practice, a major in operational research. He subsequently received training as a surgeon and then spent six years on the overseas medical staff of Shell Petroleum.

Searching for an expanded occupational medical role, Dr. Wright joined the Institute of Directors in 1958 to found the Institute of Directors Medical Centre in London. In one sense the Institute of Directors could be thought of as a counterpart of the National Association of Manufacturers in the United Kingdom. There he has subsequently developed the only English clinic specializing in problems of executive health. He is medical advisor to the Institute and thus has a very broad contact with the occupational problems of hundreds of industries in England. As director of a growing staff of physicians, he is particularly concerned with the environmental and psychosocial problems of the businessman. He has at times, however, been known to step out of this role and, in 1964, was instrumental in organizing the first International Congress on Social Psychiatry in London. His or-

ganized data on the stressful problems in executive life and the symptoms of his patients represent a unique resource in the world today for those interested in the medical problems of British industry. Since he is a frequent visitor to the United States and familiar with comparative studies in this country, Dr. Wright was asked to compare and contrast the health of the British and the American executives.

I asked Dr. Wright: How many management people evaluated at the IOD Medical Centre present psychiatric disorders? What symptoms are seen? How does this compare with lower level workers? How do you suggest such medical problems be handled by your patients? To what extent do these emotional reactions stem from the work situation, to what extent from off-the-job pressures, and to what extent from the personalities of the individuals in question? Are there cultural differences between executives in the United Kingdom and the executives in the United States that determine the stresses to which they react? If so, what may they be?

Dr. Wright asked that it be made explicitly clear that the views presented in his discussion are his alone and do not necessarily represent the official views of the organization for which he works.

The Institute of Directors was founded in 1903 and given a Royal Charter in 1906, but has expanded from 400 members in 1951 to nearly 45,000 today. To be eligible for election to membership the man, or woman—there are in fact nearly 1000 female members—has to be a director of a company within the meaning of the U.K. Companies Act. If elected he then joins the Institute as an individual and in his own right. There is no corporate membership although several or all the members of a board may, and often do, join—but individually.

This means that the IOD, although representing directors as a group, has much greater flexibility in policy decisions than it would if there were corporate membership with official representatives on whom decisions were binding. Probably because of differences in company structure, there is no direct American equivalent of the IOD. For the purposes of this presentation, it will be convenient to think of the Institute as an organization of executive vice presidents.

The Confederation of British Industries, recently formed by the amalgamation of the old Federation of British Industries, British Employers' Confederation, and National Union of Manufacturers, is the formal body representing industry and may be seen as a counterpart of the Trades Union Congress that represents the workers.

The Institue of Directors has three main functions:

1. To act as a representative body for directors as a whole. Because of its flexible organization and personal membership, it is in a strong position to react rapidly to events and problems, and thus to bring pressure on the government and to influence public opinion generally.

2. To advise and inform its members over the whole spectrum of problems involving not only management but the interrelations of industry and the community. To this end, it provides a monthly magazine, the *Director,* and a number of specialized advisory bureaus on such things as pensions, insurance, tax, labor relations, retirement, and the arts. There is also a language laboratory and a medical center.

3. To provide club and social facilities, rooms for meetings and meals.

THE MEDICAL CENTRE

The IOD Medical Centre was opened in June 1964 and has a staff of two full-time and ten visiting doctors. It is the only "clinic" in Britain specializing in the occupational health problems of the business man. We seek to combine the usual medical checkup, with its battery of prediagnostic screening tests, with a searching environmental examination. We feel that it is the relationship between the individual (his personality, strengths, and weaknesses) and his environment (work, home, and leisure) that largely determines not only health and disease, but also effectiveness and productivity.

Occupational health is concerned with the "why" rather than the "what" of illness, and as health is more than the mere absence of disease, this approach allows the practice of both clinical and environmental medicine. By operating in this way, it is possible not only to advise the individual but if all the executives from an organization are seen, it is also possible to express an opinion on the climate within the organization as it is experienced by the individuals it constitutes. Thus, given the right terms of reference and a high degree of mutual confidence, stressful situations can be defined, exposed, and discussed.

Currently the Medical Centre is seeing about 3000 "managers" per year. Forty percent of them come as individual members of the IOD and the rest as picked men chosen by their firms. These groups include both directors and executives.

THE STRUCTURE OF BRITISH COMPANIES

Britain probably has a much higher proportion of small and medium-sized units than does America. Giant corporations, like Shell, Unilever, and ICI do exist and many large American firms have operating companies in Britain and Europe. But the characteristic unit is the limited company run by a board of directors who are elected by and responsible to the shareholders, for the good management of the enterprise.

Directors may be full-time and executive, or part-time and on more than one board. There has been a tendency for the average company to have a board of full-time working directors who in fact double in the role of policy maker and executive or line manager. This double role tends to cause confusion in role awareness and to a lack of distinction between the implications of policy-making and execution.

The very large companies tend to be divisionalized on a semiautonomous basis. Divisional managers may or may not be on the main board, which in turn may or may not have additional part-time outside directors.

In practice, the British director, and hence the typical IOD member, is more akin to the American vice president than he is to the American board member, who has much less responsibility for the day-to-day conduct of his company's affairs.

Comments in this chapter are thus based on our experience with directors and managers who will be referred to from now on as executives.

Present trends in British management are toward a more clearly defined two-tier structure of upper advisory and policy-defining, and lower executive and line management. It is, however, perhaps worth noting that 26 percent of IOD members started in a family firm and 23 percent now have a controlling interest in the firm. Family or tribal warfare can, in our experience, be a pregnant cause of both stress and inefficiency.

ATTITUDES TO MANAGEMENT IN BRITAIN AND AMERICA

It is platitudinously necessary to make the point that in analyzing any basis of behavior or in looking for causes of stress, behavior is largely determined by cultural and community traditions and attitudes. There is no doubt that community attitudes to business and to success in business are vastly different in our two countries.

British management and the industry it represents is currently being criticized as amateur, relatively unprofessional, and consequently less efficient than it need be. One of the main reasons for this is that a career in business in Britain is not yet regarded as a high status or well-regarded activity. For this and other reasons, there have been, until very recently, extremely limited opportunities for a recognized professional training.

Looking, on the other hand, at American business life, one cannot avoid the impression that professionalism is in danger of becoming an end in itself, so that its practitioners go into it expecting to be stressed and ulcerated. Because this and other similar attitudes have fed back into community life, there is a correspondingly much greater acceptance of and reliance on psychiatric advice.

The effects of this difference in approach to the philosophy of management is perhaps seen in its purest form in some of the American subsidiaries of firms operating in Britain. In dealing medically and environmentally with their English executives, one cannot sometimes help but gain the impression that professional management techniques have become an end in themselves, bearing little practical relation to the local problems that have to be solved immediately. They can therefore be a considerable source of stress and overwork.

In America, to succeed in business is the goal of every office boy and every father's son. It is an okay and desirable activity and the trappings and symbols of success are equally desirable. In England, however, although the outward manifestations of a high income are desirable and indeed prestigious, they are still more than a little suspect if earned in the city or on the Stock Exchange. This, and the lack of "graduate professionalism," makes British business appear more amateur and empirical than it really is. This sort of comparison is doubly dangerous, particularly when it is made on foreign soil, because it inevitably leads to emphasizing the weaknesses, and because of lack of space, neglecting the virtues and strengths. British economy is currently at a low ebb and there is a lot that is bad about our management. But we are leaderless rather than decadent, and there are plenty of success stories.

It is, however, true to say that we are only beginning to attract the best university graduates into industry. In addition, there is a serious shortage of recognized training facilities—and that well-known invisible export, the Harvard case study, is currently spreading, rashlike, over Europe.

This difference in attitude to a career in business is well demonstrated by some figures we recently collected about the training and background of our IOD members.

Their ages vary from thirty to over seventy with 34 percent being between forty-five and fifty-five. Only 18 percent have a university degree, but to be fair it should also be noted that 40 percent have a formal professional qualification—in engineering, law, accountancy, and so on. Of those who went to the university more studied science than the arts.

Only 21 percent have attended a formal management training course (62 percent for top, 27 percent for middle, and 5 percent for junior management). Of these only 7 percent have a formal certificate or diploma of management and a third did not rate the holding of such a diploma as being of value in taking on new staff.

The attitudes that lie behind this situation are a far cry from the cachet value of the Harvard Master of Business Administration. But in practice, although British management is done more by ear than by the case study, it is a great deal better than might be thought from this superficial lack of professionalism. It is true that no major university yet runs a formal degree course in business studies, but this situation is rapidly changing and the IOD alone now sponsors three senior teaching posts, and business schools are cropping up rather too quickly for the peace of mind of those who care about the content and methods of education. Another major feature that distinguishes the English executive from his European and American cousins is his relatively low salary. The London *Times* published in February 1966 a series of comparisons of executive incomes, both gross and net after tax. England was a long way at the bottom of the league. But currently even the Labour government is beginning to realize that with taxation at its present high level, there may be a need to reconsider the role of financial incentives in the efficient functioning of what is a predominantly free enterprise economy.

We are all the slaves of our traditions and our prejudices. If the diseases people get are related to the lives they lead, and we strongly believe that they are, cultural elements must be important, especially for stress diseases. For this and other reasons, the English executive finds it more difficult than the American to accept the fact that he and his firm may have a stress problem. It also has the advantage of making our "rat race" a good deal less hectic than yours.

In this respect, it has already been said—but it is worth reemphasis—one cannot help making an outsider's observation that the American executive is brought up to have such a good opinion of himself and his contribution, that he almost expects to be stressed and ulcerated. Indeed, he is surrounded by doctors and psychiatrists who are continually taking his metaphorical pulse and advising him on the solution of his conflicts.

Obviously, this is a gross and slightly mischievous over-simplification of a complex situation, but there is a vast difference between our two countries in the approach to and the acceptance of psychological and behavioral advice in both industry and the community. As demand largely conditions supply, there are in England, compared with America, extraordinarily few behaviorists, including psychotherapists, who are able to advise industry. But for this and similar reasons the English businessman finds it difficult to admit that he might have a medical, let alone a stress or personality problem. And this marks a very fundamental difference in the basic attitudes of the two groups we are now discussing. Which in fact is the better off medically in the end, is impossible to say.

DISEASE PATTERNS IN BRITISH WORKERS AND EXECUTIVES

There is currently considerable anxiety in Europe and America about the escalation of absentee rates. It is becoming apparent that the generous provision of welfare and medical services leads to a serious rise in so-called sickness. That this tends to fall in periods of unemployment and rise with prosperity, has recently been demonstrated by Enterline in the States and Morris in England. Death rates, which are a more accurate measure of serious disease, remain more or less constant. See Table I.

In Britain, days lost from certified sickness (more than three days by insured working men) has gone up from 204 million in 1953 to 231 million in 1963. So-called mental dis-

TABLE 1

SICK ABSENCE (1956) AND EMPLOYMENT RATES (1960); SELECTED WESTERN NATIONS*

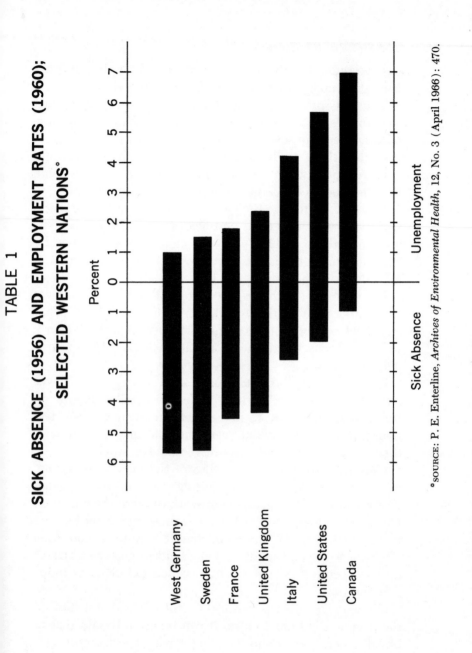

*SOURCE: P. E. Enterline, *Archives of Environmental Health*, 12, No. 3 (April 1966): 470.

ease accounts for about 10 percent of this absence and has itself gone up by 2 percent over the same period.

Thus, in spite of a rising standard of living and all that this implies, sickness is increasing rather than diminishing. Clearly there are several possible explanations of this trend; first, that there really is more disease which requires and gets treatment when this is economically available; second, that the people concerned are not fully motivated to work and can afford to take time off. This is abetted by the readiness with which medical certificates and sickness benefits are currently available. This implies a high acceptance by the community of sickness as a respectable occupation; an attitude aided historically by the medical profession.

But overall I see this as a sociological problem of motivation, rather than a strictly medical problem of sickness. That statistical nonentity, the average British worker, loses nearly fourteen days a year off work and his wife or sister approximately three weeks.

Executives, on the other hand, have a very much lower sickness experience. We have collected detailed figures on this which show that 89 percent of our members take less than a week off in several years and that only 6 percent of them have ever been away for more than two weeks.

Here then we have the paradox of the managerial group, who can afford to be ill and to take more or less as much time off as they want, staying at work through thick or thin. Our medical experience tells us that these men would in fact be fitter and possibly more effective if they took more time off and had proper holidays. They tend to get—as a stress/fatigue symptom—what we have called delusions of indispensability.

We manage to keep reasonably full medical statistics on the people using our Centre. It can be usefully said that in broad general terms and covering a wide spectrum of ages from thirty to seventy, we find something medically wrong with a third of the people seen.

Clinically cardiovascular disease, particularly in a preclinical or presymptomatic form, predominates, and is found in 25 percent of the total. Overt disease—some of it prognostically trivial, but nevertheless incapacitating—was found in a further 18 percent. It is worth noting also that, contrary to popular belief, peptic ulceration was very uncommon and is definitely not a businessman's disease in Britain. Alcoholism does not seem to be anything like the problem that it is in America. Figures are impossible to get but we certainly do not see or have referred to us as many as ten cases a year. It may be that we are missing a number but close contact with colleagues in industrial medicine confirms that this is not a major problem with us.

So-called stress conditions are notoriously difficult to define or measure, but using reasonably stringent criteria, 17 percent of the whole group was considered to be suffering from stress symptoms. In these stressed people 65 percent was thought to arise from work, 23 percent domestic, and 8 percent mixed. Four percent had serious mental disease. In 2000 cases analysed in detail, 12 percent of the men under forty, 13 percent of the forty to forty-nine group, 14 percent of the fifty to sixty, and 8 percent of the over-sixty age group were stressed. Breaking these down into firms and individuals, there was more stress in the younger executives who came individually and more in the older men who came through their firms. Most of this stress was manifested by psychosomatic symptoms but there was also an appreciable interference with performance.

Table II shows this interesting comparison very clearly. In it can be seen the fact that it appears to be the younger people working in small firms, and the older people in large

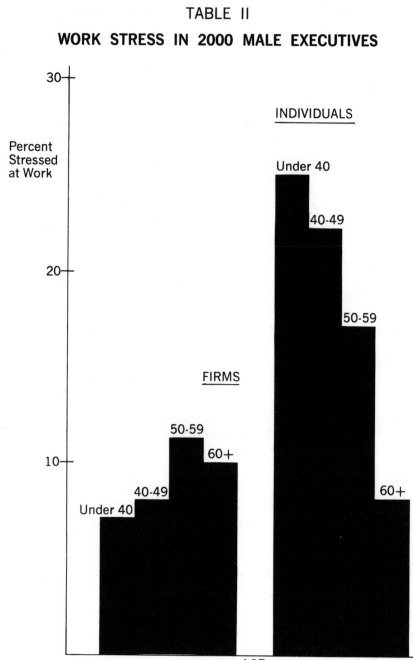

TABLE II

WORK STRESS IN 2000 MALE EXECUTIVES

firms who appear to be stressed. This can, perhaps rather teleologically, be explained by the fact that the relatively untrained youngster working with inadequate support finds the going hard. As he gets older, he presumably either succeeds or is selected out. The man in the larger organization, on the other hand, is supported by the hierachy while he is young but is currently finding it difficult to adapt to change and the competition of the better trained youngsters, as he gets older.

Interestingly and not unexpectedly, there is a positive correlation between stress and heavy cigarette smoking and also the stressed group admitted to an appreciably higher alcohol intake. More stressed men had cardiographic abnormalities than the nonstressed group, and they also had a significantly raised mean systolic blood pressure. There was no correlation with raised cholesterol levels, but cigarette smokers as a whole had higher cholesterol levels than had nonsmokers or light-smokers. These points are illustrated in Tables III (page 183) and IV (page 185).

CAUSES AND EFFECTS OF EXECUTIVE STRESS

It is a legitimate generalization to say that a byproduct of professionalism in American management is the expectation of being stressed and ulcerated. Because he has long been regarded as a valuable asset, the United States executive has been looked after by complicated medical examinations. In Britain, however, it is still extremely difficult to get the executive to even admit that his health matters. Health maintenance is only now, and gradually in the larger firms, becoming accepted. But there is as yet little acceptance of the importance of psychosomatic causes of symptoms and little reliance on the contribution that psychiatrists and behavioral scientists can make to the running of an enterprise. This makes the British executive reluctant to admit that he is stressed and very hesitant about seeking psychiatric help. But in spite of this, the Englishman is almost certainly more placid, less aggressively competitive and if he is stressed it may be for less sophisticated reasons.

Stress is difficult to define precisely, largely because it tends to be both measured and thought about purely in terms of its ill effects on the individual. This leads to the total neglect of the beneficial aspects of stress, or indeed the inevitability of some stress or challenge in the maintenance of biological life and effectiveness. The term stress derives from engineering and implies an inherent capacity to resist or stand up to a defined amount of strain. Increasing the loading on a girder beyond a certain point will inevitably bend it. Individuals too have their breaking point and if this is exceeded, they also bend or break.

In practice, various psychosomatic, and largely unconscious, defense mechanisms are thrown into play. These tend to lead the individual to opt out of the stressful situation and can be regarded as a direct result of the interplay between the individual and his immediate environment. Clearly this is a complicated situation in which the individual's reaction is the final common pathway between his training, attributes, and personality and the various specific and cultural pressures that the environment—work, home, and community—are putting on to him. We have found it convenient to express this as the personality/environment equation: a dynamic, constantly changing, and reactive relationship between the individual, acting as a totality, and his whole environment.

If the equation remains reasonably in balance, the individual makes the grade, derives satisfaction and motivation

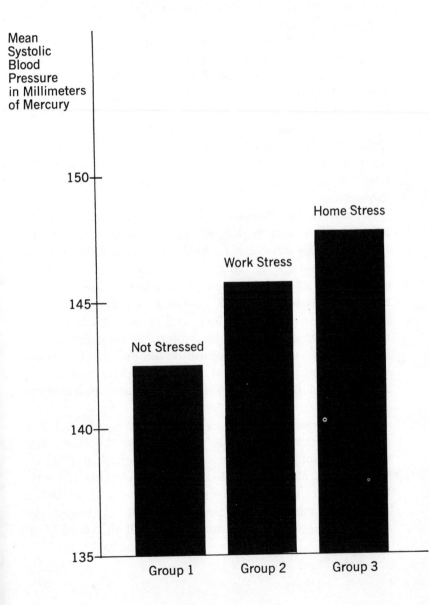

TABLE III

**EFFECT OF STRESS ON SYSTOLIC BLOOD PRESSURE
IN 2000 MALE EXECUTIVES**

from so doing and remains well and healthy. If, on the other hand, the situation becomes too much for him, he goes out of balance and exhibits stress symptoms that reduce either his long- or short-term effectiveness. It also causes disease as it is classically known.

A stressed individual can thus be defined as one whose personality/environment equation is out of balance—the environment is too much for him. Implicit in this definition is the realization that the right amount of stress or challenge is both good and, indeed, essential. Also implicit is the necessity to realize that the stress situation is, and can only be, highly personal in its effects. It must be analysed in terms of *this man, this situation:* but both must be looked at as totalities. It is naïve to think that one only takes half of oneself to the office.

Cardiovascular disease—high blood pressure and coronary thrombosis—is the largest killer of middle-aged men in Britain. The factors currently believed to contribute to coronary proneness are, in random order, genetic or hereditary, obesity, lack of exercise, cigarette smoking, a raised blood cholesterol, stress, overwork (defined as doing the wrong things in the wrong priorities), and so on. The major and relevant point here is that the majority of these are behavioral reactions within the control of the individual and are therefore both reflections of the personality/environment situation and likely to respond to treatment and analysis only along these lines.

Certainly one can relieve an ulcer by giving alkalis, but it can only be cured by dealing with its cause. Another major and vital point about stress is that, although all individuals have their breaking point, the manifestation of this will vary. We do not yet know why one man gets dyspepsia, another a skin disease, insomnia, or hypertension. This is, of course, the reason for our, now almost fanatical, belief that to help an

TABLE IV

FACTORS RELATED TO STRESS IN 2000 MALE EXECUTIVES

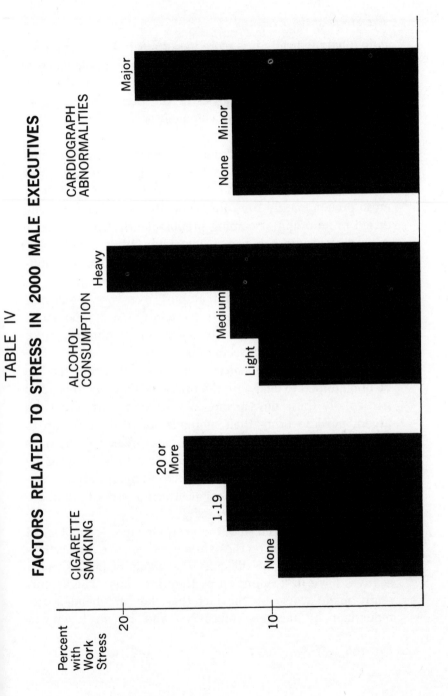

individual medically it is more important to know why he is ill than what is wrong with him; and this points the value of our environmental approach to executive stress and executive function. It is by analysis of the personality/environment equation that one can comment on the climate within organizations.

It is against this background, or within this overriding philosophy, that we have looked at some of the causes of executive stress in Britain. We found that over half of it arose predominantly from the work situation; the rest being mixed in its origin or coming predominantly from domestic unbalance. Some too comes inevitably from people who have an unstable or psychopathic personality and are unsuitable for the job—a reflection of poor selection procedures.

It must be remembered that pure overwork, while not necessarily a cause of stress, certainly lowers the stress threshold. Common causes of stress, or manifestations of inadequacy, would thus seem to be:

1. *A lack of professionalism.* This means that they tend to be ill-equipped to deal with the problems that face them and particularly those now arising in very acute form from the urgent need to bring their methods and techniques up to date. A major benefit of education, and indeed perhaps its main function, is to equip the individual to learn what he does not know. It is not surprising that so many executives—30 percent of whom left school at fifteen or sixteen—find the acquisition of new skills so stressful.

2. *Age.* As has been said, the need for rapid technological change bears hardest on the extremes of age. We are particularly impressed by the difficulty that many of our older executives have in keeping up as they get older. This is currently made worse by the fact that they are being made redundant by mergers, takeovers, and by an inevitable

streamlining of management teams. There is little doubt, as has been shown by the activities of the well-known internationally active consultant firms like McKinsey, that British management has often been overstaffed.

There is a great deal of very real and entirely valid anxiety among older executives about their chances of economic survival. This is a legitimate and understandable cause of stress. It has also led us, when dealing with our older patients, to pay increasing attention to the problems of retirement and to preparation for retirement.

3. *Family firms.* Running any business is difficult enough, but to do this in a family context is to increase the conflict that inevitably occurs between generations. Reference has already been made to the high proportion of family firms in Britain, a proportion that is increased by shares held in family trusts or by widows and sisters.

Tribal warfare of this type is a not uncommon and often quite unnecessary source of stress in management. Similarly the son of the family coming into the business is subjected to stresses he would not experience as a management trainee in an "alien" firm.

4. *Role ambiguity and lack of definition of tasks and responsibilities.* British company structure tends to blur the boundaries between policy-making and the administrative implications of carrying out this policy. Similarly there is, arising from the lack of professional definition within organizations, a failure to construct situations and write job descriptions so that the individual can define himself and his tasks in reasonable relation to the "whole." Both these are a prevalent cause of stress and frustration.

5. *"The wrong person for the climate."* It tends to be forgotten that the avoidance of undue stress depends on putting the right man into a reasonably congenial situation.

Both firms and individuals tend to drift along and suffer accordingly. We find ourselves, with increasing frequency, advising both parties that one or the other is wrong for one of them. The needs of both change with time; the youngster who develops a new enterprise is not necessarily the man to consolidate it and the older consolidator is seldom the right man to initiate the next leap forward.

6. *Social competence and class.* Many successful British and American executives came from humble origins and left school early. In Britain particularly they often find that the growing demands of social, as apart from technical or professional performance, are demanding and stressful. Speaking and appearing in public, which tend to come naturally to the public school and university graduate, often place a severe strain on the self-made man. This cause of stress can be accentuated when the man's wife, whom he may have married young and who came from his original background, makes the grade less successfully than he does.

7. *The frustration of legislative interference.* In prewar England it was, on the whole, possible to buy a plot of land, put up a factory, subject to local building regulations, and one was in business. Now that development is zoned and taxation differentiates between various types of staff, running a business is much more complicated and uncertain. This inability to plan freely seems increasingly to be a cause, if not of stress, at least of profound and debilitating frustration.

8. *Lack of insight into motivation and behavior.* To succeed in or to survive the inevitable stress and conflict of business life is a businessman's source of satisfaction and gratification. If the British executive, because he is less sophisticated, is less aware of the pressures and conflicts that are likely to stress him, his stress may be less complicated in its manifestations and easier to deal with clinically. Cer-

tainly we find that our environmental approach helps to develop simple insights into the motivation of stress symptoms. Similarly, the environmentally oriented doctor can influence the climate within an organization so as to reduce the stress potential to the mutual benefit of both.

IV

Labor, Management, and Mental Health

14 Labor-Management Relations and Mental Health

Hyman J. Weiner

Since the mid-1940's an increasing number of labor unions have developed mental health programs. In general, these have been independent activities developed apart from management. Indeed, labor has been highly suspicious of management-sponsored mental health activities. Unions' statements on the subject strongly imply that the psychiatrist and psychologist on any company payroll are employed solely for the purposes of manipulating union members toward management identification. The feeling has been expressed that any mental health program must not be paternalistic, should not be used to undermine the grievance procedure or in any other way subvert the union movement. These cautions influence labor's attitude and have resulted in few programs under joint union-management sponsorship. Each of the union programs has differed slightly from its fellows. Some involve the services of a psychiatrist in a union-sponsored clinic or hospital. Others involve administering insurance funds that provide psychiatric care for members. There is only one which is concerned primarily with the rehabilitation of the psychiatric casualty. Dr. Hyman J. Weiner is director of that project.

At the Sidney Hillman Health Center in New York, the mental health rehabilitation program was an outgrowth of a physical rehabilitation project. The staff of the project goes out into the factories and works with union representatives and into the union halls where they are visible and immediately available to all workers. Cooperation by management has been extremely high. The health center and the mental health project serve members of the Amalgamated Clothing Workers Union.

Hyman Weiner received a doctorate in social welfare at Columbia University and is currently on the part-time faculty of the Columbia University School of Social Work. He is also a consultant at several Veterans Administration Hospitals and a consultant to a number of labor unions in areas of mental health and rehabilitation.

In this chapter I asked Dr. Weiner to describe his fascinating program of rehabilitation. Further, I asked: What can union negotiators and management representatives learn from contemporary mental health rehabilitation concepts? Are there ways in which clinical and behavioral science skills can be applied more successfully to an ongoing relationship between a union and an employer? How do the "roles people play" interfere with the successful resolution of labor-management conflicts? This chapter represents his thoughtful response.

There is evidence of growing interest in locating and controlling factors in the work environment that may be associated with mental health and mental illness. We are at that point in time when at least this issue has been placed on the social agenda. Let us be careful, however, not to assume that the road to success has already been charted by the early pioneers of industrial medicine. Although similarities exist, mental health in industry presents a qualitatively different set of concerns. For instance, employees' physical health, no doubt, benefits from the modern industrial plants that are increasingly more airy, sanitary and safety conscious. On the other hand, the resulting emotional climate may be equally antiseptic in these rationalized, efficient but often more impersonal environments.

If we are to make progress in this very difficult and complicated terrain of mental health in industry, let us try to identify some of the obstacles interfering with this pursuit, and in the process share the results of the action programs currently under way. In this discussion I will be drawing upon my experience as director of a mental health-rehabilitation program in the men's clothing industry. This is a labor-management effort at the Sidney Hillman Health Center, serving members of the New York Joint Board of the Amalgamated Clothing Workers of America. It is supported, in part, by grants from the National Institute of Mental Health and the Vocational Rehabilitation Administration.

For the past five years, a staff consisting of social workers, nurses, psychiatrists, and general physicians have been attempting to help mentally and physically disabled clothing workers maintain their jobs and their ability to function. Our work brings us into union halls, factories, and the community. It is another example of labor-management cooperation in the men's clothing industry—but not without its problems and strains. Although our primary goal is to demonstrate and test ways of rehabilitating ill people, we have accumulated some impressions and hunches that pertain to labor-management relations and mental health.

LABOR-MANAGEMENT CONFLICT

Both labor and management have much to gain from turning their attention to mental health, but in doing so, must be prepared to face new areas of conflicting interests. We are not convinced that the mental health of employees and the interests of a company are always congruent. In the long run this may be the case, but it is not necessarily so at a given point in time or in relation to specific employees. I am sure that production would sharply decline in certain industries if some of the obsessive-compulsive employees were suddenly to solve their emotional problems. Increasingly, labor unions are asking management to take more responsibility for restructuring the jobs of mentally disabled workers, some of whom clearly are functioning on a marginal level but are long-term employees.

Labor is generally suspicious of management's interest in the mental health of its employees—for too often it has been used as a guise for antiemployee practices whether by design or unintended consequence. It appears that we are in the third round of this mental health game. The first was characterized by the "sophisticated" personnel director who came upon the scene in the post-World War II years armed with his personality tests and predictive instruments. The 1950's witnessed the industrial relations expert and his attempt to create a "happy foreman" model with its so-called benefits to the worker. Currently, the role of the medical department in industry is receiving attention as a runway from which to launch mental health programs. If labor can be involved early in these efforts, I believe, there is some chance for success. Let us begin, therefore, by identifying those areas of common ground where management and labor mutually benefit and where trust can be cultivated.

THE INDIVIDUAL WORK SETTING

Each factory appears to have its own way of dealing with the emotional problems of its employees and tends to reflect the general pattern of interpersonal relations at work. Three features of the work place, as they bear on mental health and mental illness, will be discussed in the light of our rehabilitation experience. They are (1) coping with *conflict*, (2) opportunities for *pride in workmanship*, and (3) dealing with *confidentiality*.

Successful interpersonal relations hinge in part on the way one deals with conflict. This is as true in marital relations and friendships as it is in industry. To some extent we all have been brainwashed by the notion of consensus. As a result, conflict situations tend to be viewed negatively and handled by denying their existence or responding in a disapproving manner. Admittedly, conflict is always disturbing and unsettling. It takes skill and experience to deal with it in a constructive manner. It is no accident that the role of mediator is becoming an increasingly important one in our society.

This area can be especially painful for the employer who considers himself a reasonable individual and becomes personally insulted at the "ungrateful" attitude of his employees when a conflict arises. Those of us who are parents of teenagers live daily with this dynamic. What appears to add insult to injury is when the employee asks the union shop steward to accompany him to a grievance meeting. Our view is that this very process contributes to a mentally healthy problem-solving climate in the work place. It is a vital mechanism through which change can be lived with and adjusted to. The inability to face conflict squarely generally leads to many difficulties. Anger builds up and becomes directed either toward the other party or toward oneself. In any event, it seriously blocks communication.

A good deal of our clinical activity in rehabilitation has been directed at helping the emotionally ill workers test out different ways of dealing with conflict on the job. In a sense we function as the psychological mediators between employee and employer, and at times between union member and union. In one case, a docile, quiet and inwardly angry worker began to express himself more openly. Although we considered this to be a change for the better, the production manager was disappointed in this shift from what he described as "a quiet man, easy to get along with." In a number of situations our goal is to help a worker control his anger more effectively. We have a number of examples in our records of clothing workers who were helped by the type of labor-management cooperation that addressed itself to aiding the patient to control his impulses. Unfortunately, the label troublemaker is attached too readily to the worker who becomes involved in a conflict situation. No doubt there are some employees, as well as some employers, who enjoy head-on collisions, but by and large, the ability to deal with conflict demands a good deal of self-esteem and considered judgment. Too often, management is more concerned with who raises the grievance rather than with the merits of the grievance itself.

A second dimension of the work place of interest to our rehabilitation team is the extent to which pride in workmanship is cultivated and encouraged in each factory. Pride in one's accomplishments is not necessarily restricted to the highly skilled worker, though opportunities for creative labor are greater for the craftsman. We are as concerned with the feelings of satisfaction of a job well done by the semiskilled sewing machine operator and the clerk in the office. We know of many severely mentally ill clothing workers able to function on the job partly because of the self-esteem nourished in the particular factories where they work. Two attitudes shared by employers and employees alike often limit opportunities to make it on the job for workers with mental problems. Rather than focusing on what a person can do despite his emotional problem, the primary interest is usually the nature of the illness and whether the worker has been hospitalized.

Industrial environments most helpful to our rehabilitation

program have been those that make realistic demands to function at the highest level possible. Management in these settings makes gradual but consistent demands that build on previous successes. Rather than "cover up" for the emotionally ill employee, they make honest assessments of the quality of work and share it with the employee. If there is any one lesson to be learned from our rehabilitation experience, it is that a worker with a mental problem should be viewed first as a worker and the illness considered only as a potential obstacle to quality performance. Labels of "ex-hospital patient" or "schizophrenic," though clinically relevant, have become meaningless to us in our vocational rehabilitation activity. Strange as it seems, severity of illness has not been a reliable guage of success on the job. Obviously, for those at the extreme end of pathology, one can predict vocational failure but not for the vast majority of our patients. Emphasis has been shifting steadily to what an emotionally ill person *can do* rather than to what illness he has.

The ability to use conflict as an opportunity to improve work relations and the creation of a climate that encourages pride in accomplishments are no easy undertakings. This brings us to the third dimension, namely, dealing with confidentiality. Secrecy flourishes best in an atmosphere of mistrust. It actually becomes the currency of interpersonal relations. Within this type of milieu the person with a mental problem suffers most—for above all he needs trusting relationships. Although he may pay the highest price, the "007" type of setting corrodes the mental health of everyone in the work place.

We found that the person with emotional problems has often shared his difficulties with those he trusts in the shop. Successful rehabilitation has occurred when these "significant others" are involved in the treatment program by working closely with mental health professionals.

Confidentiality is a two-edged sword. It offers some protection from embarrassment, but often limits the extent to which the employee with work problems can be helped by others in the factory or office. Employers and supervisors can cultivate trust among personnel by working closely with union officials and shop stewards where the ill worker gives his consent—which occurs more frequently than we realize. As often as not, it is our discomfort rather than the ill person's plea for confidentiality that accounts for a good deal of the supposed secrecy. Our experience indicates that many workers with emotional problems who discuss their difficulties with each other welcome the participation and interest of management.

It is not suggested that an employer should break the rules of confidence and shout from the roof tops about a particular worker's emotional problems. But neither should we restrict the sharing of information from those the ill employee already is open with and wants to have involved. Admittedly, it is a delicate issue—but we have tended to err on the side of too much confidentiality. Recently we circulated a simple questionnaire in a clothing factory inquiring about the mental health problems of workers or members of their families. Many responded honestly and openly to what appeared to be very personally threatening questions. It also became clear to us that many counseled each other about the various medical and therapeutic approaches used.

TOWARD CONSTRUCTIVE SOLUTIONS

The above discussion merely touched on a few dimensions of the work place we have found relevant in our vocational rehabilitation program. We are convinced that helping emotionally disabled workers can be one way of contributing to effective labor-management relations. Both parties are needed to help maintain disabled workers on the job. Invariably, an honest discussion of a worker's problem on the job opens some interesting questions for the labor-management group itself. It usually begins by kidding within the group with the statement that "we all need some help." Gradually serious discussion unfolds around ways of handling anger, making demands upon people in a nonbelligerent way, and the like. In general, we have not found educational programs to be very useful, and therefore, are partial to the approach that tries to tease out mental health educational issues around the discussion of a specific person in trouble.

Undoubtedly, labor unions are becoming more sensitive to mental health issues—whether at the collective-bargaining table in seeking fringe benefits or at grievance meetings handling a worker's complaint. Labor shares with management many misconceptions about mental illness—but both also are very realistic about designing mental health approaches appropriate to their sphere of influence. Both groups are faced with constantly changing work situations. As noted earlier, the movement toward more rationalized work flow creates as many new problems as it solves. It would be interesting for management to evaluate its policies, both explicit and implicit, in the areas of personnel and use of manpower along some of the dimensions noted above. Simultaneously, union officials will be forced to do some self-examination, for they, too are faced with similar dynamics. Recently, you may have noticed how often union members have disavowed their own leaders' recommendations. The goal of cultivating commitment to organizations is inherent in our pluralistic society. Insights and experience from the mental health field can be helpful—but let us be cautious.

Although it may come as a shock to some of us, I have it on excellent authority that the mental health professional will not be the one to break new ground in the field of labor-management relations. There is much he can contribute in this arena, but he is no "music man" who can solve complicated industrial relations problems with mental health tools. Investing him with magical powers will surely lead to disenchantment.

In these changing times, for mental health as well as for industry, there may be new alternatives available to us. Each industry and labor management group must go its own way—but I believe each can develop some general approaches to mental health programs. For some, this resource can be available through an industrial medical department or a jointly sponsored labor-management health program. For the first time, however, opportunities exist for industry to tie in with community mental health programs. The developments outlined in this book can be linked up with the efforts of industry. If we keep our goals modest, perhaps by starting to help workers in trouble, we may create the preconditions for other types of consultation services. The labor-management arena is faced with an extremely complicated set of tasks. The addition of mental health and behavioral science insights may contribute in a small way to finding more effective solutions.

Finally, there is another way in which industry can contribute to community mental health developments and in turn reap certain rewards. Involvement with community social problems is a legitimate way to earn a reputation as being a concerned and responsible industrial institution. Even if a company never develops its own mental health service or a cooperative relationship with a community mental health facility, it can play a role in promoting better mental health in the geographical region in which it functions. It could be a new arena and common task for labor-management cooperation.

15 Psychiatric Disability: The UAW Response

Melvin A. Glasser

Blue-collar workers, who are often union members, have for many reasons been deprived of adequate treatment for psychiatric disorders. At least this is the judgment of many union spokesmen. Further description of both union and employer preconceptions of mental health problems will provide the reader with a greater understanding of the reasons for this deprivation. This chapter also describes a pioneering prepaid psychiatric care program for two and three-quarter million UAW members and their dependents designed to answer many of the prior inadequacies.

Melvin A. Glasser, director of the Social Security Department of the UAW since 1963, has been responsible for this union activity. He came to the UAW from Brandeis University where he was dean of University Resources and visiting professor at the Graduate School for Advanced Studies in Social Welfare. Before that, he was executive vice president of the National Foundation for Infantile Paralysis, serving as administrative director for the nationwide Salk poliomyelitis vaccine field trials and directing studies that led to the organization's expanded interest in patients with birth defects. Mr. Glasser also served as executive director of

Labor, Management, and Mental Health

President Truman's Mid-Century White House Conference on Children and Youth and as associate chief of the United States Children's Bureau. He is past president of the International Federation of Social Workers and former chairman of the Executive Committee of the National Health Council. He was awarded an honorary degree of Doctor of Laws by Adelphi University for "distinguished contributions to the advancement of the social sciences." For his work in organizing health and welfare services abroad, he has been decorated by the governments of the Netherlands, Denmark, Finland, Argentina, and Czechoslovakia.

I asked Mr. Glasser to reflect a union view of psychiatric disability and to describe the new UAW prepayment coverage for psychiatric illness. Further, I asked: What might union expectations be of employers when a union member develops an incapacitating mental disorder? Have there been joint union-management activities in this area? In the past there has been some suspicion of company-sponsored mental health programs. Is this still the case? Mr. Glasser's erudition is clearly apparent as he responds to these questions.

After a study of the Cheney Silk Mills in Connecticut, Dr. C. C. Burlingame reported, "During that time we established the fact that emotional attitudes on the part of employees toward their employment, their foremen, their fellow workers and the machines in the great textile industry were more responsible for a greater loss in dollars and cents than accidents and contagion." This report was made in 1916. Fifty years later many persons in our country are newly discovering the same information.

Perhaps through the attention this volume stimulates there will be accelerated recognition of the problems highlighted by Dr. Burlingame—problems that have been greatly intensified in American industry. Various studies show not only a continuing increase in mental breakdown in the general population, but in fact a much greater rate of breakdown and a lower rate of recovery among blue-collar workers and their families. As the studies of Dr. Arthur Kornhauser of Wayne State University have demonstrated, the proportion of workers having good mental health consistently decreases as one moves down the line from the skilled workers to the semiskilled and unskilled workers. The speed of the mechanically paced line, the lack of opportunity to alter work load to meet fatigue; the inability to control quantity, the restrictions on freedom of movement, the anonymous atmosphere of the assembly lines, the limitations on communication because of noise, heat, and pressure— these and other factors have been cited by Blauner and others to explain why there is little job satisfaction, none of the group identification that the sociologists point to as a psychological value of work, little feeling of pride in or loyalty to the company, and precious little challenge to initiative or imagination.

A recent study of blue-collar workers in the Group Health Association in Washington, D.C., indicated that stress from the work situation affected 31 percent of the males who presented psychiatric problems, and stress from the combined work and home situation affected 11 percent of the group.

The combination then of the multiplying problems of tension and stress upon blue-collar workers, much of which derives from the frustrations of work rather than its satisfactions, added to the pressures of daily living created by our societal structure and the times in which we live, when combined with economic limitations that denied many workers access to competent treatment, convinced the leadership of the UAW in 1964 that the already extensive health benefits available to its members and families should be augmented to include prepaid treatment for emotional disorders.

The so-called major medical insurance plans were rejected as a means of providing coverage. The use of dollar corridors and co-insurance as deterrents is unsatisfactory to workers, provides needed benefits to relatively few people and is antithetical to program goals of prevention, early diagnosis, and readily available treatment.

In considering the role of industry in these kinds of programs, it is important to understand that there is surprisingly little recognition that a worker who is sick because of an emotional problem essentially requires the same kind of job and benefit protection as a worker who is sick with a physical problem.

And when industry representatives, as well as many mental health professionals, address themselves to emotional problems on the job, as they are doing in these pages, attention is focused on the programs for the white-collar worker and the executive, with the implication that their needs and those of blue-collar workers are the same. The facts contradict this for there is a growing body of evidence that indicates the blue-collar worker has less understanding of and more resistance to psychiatric treatment, he has substantially less access to treatment resources, the problems created for him by the work situation are often quite different from those faced by the white-collar worker, and he of course usually has a much more substantial economic barrier to treatment than his better paid white-collar counterpart.

But industry has been surprisingly slow to recognize, even for white-collar workers, the existence of and need to deal with what two Presidents of the United States have described as "America's number one health problem." In a study made two years ago of 560 companies, ten reported the use of a psychiatrist on either a full- or a part-time basis, and only fourteen more reported they used full- or part-time psychologists. Our experience in dealing with employers as we attempted to develop the benefit and to secure its underwriting through collective bargaining is instructive. The following are quotations from employer representatives with whom the program was discussed:

> Your figures about the extent of mental illness in the country may well be true, but they do not apply to our workers. They don't have the problem.

> Mental health programs may be useful for white-collar workers; production line workers probably could not benefit from the services.

> Psychiatry and psychology are very imprecise sciences; there is little evidence that these disciplines are able to help people.

> Such services if made available will only encourage malingering.

> This is the government's problem, not the employer's.

The convictions of the UAW leadership, their persuasiveness, and their willingness to invest on a priority basis a portion of their collective bargaining package in mental health programs, has now produced the first nationwide collectively bargained, in and out of hospital mental health program in industry. Furthermore, the UAW recognized that in mental illness, even more than in physical illness, the emotional stability of the members of the family was crucial to the mental health of the worker. Accordingly, care was exercised to make certain that present family benefits for physical illness, already provided in negotiated contracts, would be extended to include emotional illness. The program, which became operative in September 1966, provides coverage to some 2¾ million UAW members and their dependents in 77 communities in 34 states and the District of Columbia. Included are the following benefits:

1. Forty-five days of in-hospital care for nervous or mental conditions, including in-hospital physicians' services while hospitalized.

2. A maximum benefit of $400 per patient per calendar year will be paid for out-of-hospital care, including the following services:

   (*a*) visits for therapy in a doctor's office;

   (*b*) treatment for ambulatory patients in approved outpatient or day care programs; reimbursement for services of psychologists and psychiatric social workers as well as psychiatrists is provided in these organized plans;

   (*c*) visits in the doctor's office or outpatient clinic by members of the patient's family for counseling services;

   (*d*) group psychotherapy; and

   (*e*) psychological testing by a psychologist when prescribed by a physician.

To encourage early referral and to minimize the economic barrier to care there are no charges for the first five visits in outpatient therapy, and the patient pays 15 percent for the second five visits in a doctor's office, 30 percent for the third five visits, and 45 percent for the balance of visits, all within the $400 ceiling per year. Hospital inpatient, as well as outpatient and day-care programs are offered without charge to the patient; he pays 15 percent of the costs of one series of psychological tests.

After two years of organization the UAW negotiated program has just gotten under way. It is therefore much too soon to ascertain its impact. We are hopeful, however, that it will sensitize management to want to learn more about mental health problems of their workers, and to deepen their understanding of the impact of management policies, either favorably or unfavorably on the safeguarding of mental health. Included in this we would hope will be increased consideration for hiring the person who has recovered from mental illness, and the use of selective assignment for the worker who either demonstrates he is functioning under stress or returns to the plant after a period of mental illness. Such factors are taken into consideration in recovery from physical illness—much less so with mental illness.

Employee benefits need to be modified so that while a worker is attempting to rehabilitate himself because of mental illness his temporary disability benefits will not expire and thus provide a disincentive to rehabilitation. It should be mentioned here that experience indicates that rehabilitation of the mentally ill person actually takes somewhat less time than that of the physically ill.

The employer can help by having management and supervisory personnel understand in greater depth than they do now, ways in which they can help the rehabilitated person find his way back into the mainstream of plant life. In addition, the mental rehabilitatee, perhaps even more than the physically ill person, needs assurance that there will be a job for him when he gets well.

Management's positive attitude toward the problems of the mentally handicapped worker, can, in a negotiated mental health program, quickly be illustrated by its willingness to interpret the program to its workers and to help them find their way to treatment resources. In the past year the Chrysler Corporation has led the way in developing a cooperative program with the UAW through which the Company and the Union have jointly sponsored leadership training sessions in the Company's plants around the country. The new mental health benefits were interpreted to management and supervisory personnel, as well as to Union members. They are being helped to understand how to identify problems of emotional illness and how to help workers seek out treatment resources now available to them as a result of the collective bargaining agreements.

A major function that employers can fulfill is to provide a work environment that contributes to mental health, or at least does not detract from it. There is much that can be done to improve working conditions so that tension, stress, noise, and heat can be reduced, so that the worker has more of a feeling of recognition as an individual, so that in some ways at least his feeling of being subservient to a machine is alleviated.

Many unions are not opposed to automation as such. They are, however, opposed to the dehumanizing effects of automation. When workers strike as they have in recent years and use slogans like "dignity on the job," they are in their way expressing frustration over many of the mentally unhealthy conditions in which they work. They also wish to share in the economic gains made possible by automation, a subject which is receiving increasing attention.

The representatives of the organized workers, the unions, also have responsibilities in helping to overcome the problems of disability caused by mental illness. They need to be prepared to set aside part of their collective bargaining money for prepaid mental health benefits, and some unions are beginning to do this. But the purchase of care is not enough. They need to work with the professions and with management in designing programs that will remove economic barriers to early diagnosis and treatment and will assure care of high quality, promptly available in dignified surroundings, from understanding professionals.

I should say here parenthetically that in my quite limited experience with the labor movement it seems reasonably clear that health services offered by employers in the plants will not meet the objectives. Workers by and large do not trust health professionals who are part of management. There is a long history of controversy with the employers' physicians and nurses whose functions in the eyes of many workers are to keep men on the job when they feel they are not well enough to work, or to deny them sickness benefits to which they feel they are entitled.

In this country, with a few minor exceptions, there has been an abysmal lack of mental health education programs for workers and their families. Perhaps it is just as well that it has been this way, for had workers overcome their resistances to securing help, they frequently would have found that it was unavailable to them. But the situation is changing. Unions, in collaboration with employers and the mental health professionals, are now in a position to do a far better job of helping their members understand the problems of mental illness and how to deal with them. In this connection the shop steward and the local union officer are key persons in the life of a union member. Properly oriented and motivated, they can be excellent referral sources as well as peculiarly well-fitted intermediaries to help the recovered worker handle his job and gain acceptance from his fellow workers.

As unions become more heavily involved in collective bargaining and in education programs in the mental health field, we should be seeing increased concern for public sector responsibility. Most of the large unions have broad and effective social action programs. Unions working alone, as well as with management, can and should be taking larger responsibility for seeing to it that there are adequate public mental health programs, that the recently authorized public community mental health centers get under way speedily, that more state hospitals become treatment facilities and not storage warehouses for the forgotten, that expanded programs for the training of mental health professionals receive community support.

The recent report on the federal-state vocational rehabilitation programs showed that in 1965, 18,296 persons who had been mentally ill were rehabilitated. This was 13.6 percent of the total rehabilitated under these public programs and the largest number and percentage of any year. Prior to acceptance for rehabilitation services, 90 percent of the rehabilitated mentally ill had no earnings. At the end of the year more than four-fifths were wage earners. It required twelve months to bring the mentally ill client from referral, to successful completion of the formal rehabilitation process. This was two months *less* than all other disability groups. On the average, purchased services for the mentally ill cost slightly over $400.

We have reached a point in American industry where the need for mental health services to prevent disability and to overcome it when it arises is clearly apparent. New programs to meet the need are developing rapidly. The costs are not high. With increasing cooperation among management, labor, and the mental health professions, it should be evident before long that the price of not doing anything is far higher in economic terms and in human costs.

16   Dependency and Work Conflict

Robert L. Meineker

This chapter is somewhat more technical than others in this volume. It introduces a psychiatrically sophisticated frame of reference offering the reader a glimpse of one man's theoretical thinking on one of the forefronts of occupational mental health. Precisely because Dr. Meineker's ideas are slightly out of step with currently accepted thought and therefore controversial, they are included as an illustration of the views of a teacher of psychiatry and consultant to industry.

Concepts of dependency in relationship to labor and management are important in the thinking of most clinicians. Technically, the resolution of conscious and unconscious conflicts involving dependency help lead an individual toward self-realization, maturity, and mental health. Stifling individual initiative, Dr. Meineker feels, fosters excessive dependency. Initiative disappears and power ends up in the hands of too few because the worker cannot accept responsibility. It is Dr. Meineker's belief that if the "Santa Claus need" cannot be resolved, the dependent worker ends up in slavery or chaos. While he may purposely overstate his case, his thoughts are provocative indeed.

Following graduation from Albany Medical College in 1945

and a subsequent internship Robert Meineker served in the Army Medical Corps in charge of public health activities in the Military Government Section in southern Japan. Subsequently trained as a pediatrician and a psychiatrist, he has been in the private practice of psychiatry in New York City since 1954. He has served as chief of the Psychiatric Outpatient Department of St. Vincent's Hospital in New York, and as an attending psychiatrist at St. Vincent's since 1955, he has been active in teaching residents in training in psychiatry. Since 1960, he has also been psychiatric consultant in the Medical Department of Continental Insurance Companies. At the national level, he is a member of the Committee on Occupational Psychiatry of the American Psychiatric Association.

I asked Dr. Meineker to consider the following questions in preparing this discussion: How do labor-management relations help foster mature, healthy, and independent functioning for organized members of the work force? How can management promote mature behavior on the part of subordinates? What specific concepts are necessary—from a psychiatric viewpoint—for readers to keep in mind as they attempt to understand labor-management conflicts? What may responsible union representatives do to better recognize the pitfalls of stereotypical responses to management demands?

In response to these questions Dr. Meineker has outlined a theory that should be interesting to the mental health professionals, well accepted by the business reader and one that will predictably arouse feelings of hostility and resistance among those in the labor movement.

Other than sex and love, work is probably the single most important way of absorbing hostility and aggression by channeling psychic energy into survival operations. Achievements at work take care of survival needs and thus lead to self-esteem. From this point of view, work is fundamental and indispensable to human life and mental health. Any

efforts to reduce its importance and amount will have a deleterious effect on the mental health and material security of
the individual and the community.

Dependency as I have observed it in helping people with
their emotional difficulties often seriously impedes successful work. I will try to describe the dynamics of dependency
and show how they create conflict at work when they are not
properly resolved.

I have chosen to focus on dependency because, in my
experience, most of the emotional problems of work stem
from unresolved dependency attitudes. This is true for the
problems of both management and labor. Their problems are
really quite inseparable and arise from similar psychody-
namic causes. Although problems from outside work involving family and friends often disturb a worker's emotional
health and interfere with his ability to work, we cannot
clearly identify them as work problems. They are problems of love or socialization. It is important to make this
distinction because work problems often exhibit different
symptomatology and usually run a different course than do
the nonwork problems. This is not surprising when one considers that work is implemented more by survival instincts
than by reproductive ones.

The concept of survival instincts requires more discussion. In work we are struggling both individually and in
groups to extract from an indifferent environment what we
need to support life: food, shelter, and protection. Because
of this preoccupation with our own survival, we are not interested in the survival of others, except as they may help us
with our own needs. Thus, at work, we are basically selfish.
This situation is quite different from the one associated
with reproductive instincts where, for satisfaction, we
must consider the needs and wishes of others. Here, if
we are to join with them in sex and in the raising of a

family many demands are ahead of our own. Therefore, when we consider that work arises from survival instincts, we must realize that the emotional problems connected with work will be self-centered, concerned with our very existence, and productive of hostility. When confronted with the rigors of survival, we may become self-centered, frightened, and hostile. We are naturally quickly carried back to patterns of thought, feeling and behavior characteristic of infancy and dependency on our parents. Therefore, we may state that emotional problems connected with work are concerned with dependency, selfishness, and hostility. Frustration of survival instincts means death. The anxiety connected with them is of a more intense variety than that related to sexual frustrations. At work, we are therefore not dealing with ordinary psychoneurotic anxiety. There is no inherent attraction to others to mitigate selfish survival drives until dependency needs have matured into group concern and one's physical being is secured.

CHILDHOOD DEPENDENCY

To develop our understanding of the dependency problem, we must start by considering its genesis. We all start life with biologically strong dependency drives which, at the time, are unconscious, natural, and appropriate. We look to our parents for nutrition and protection. Fulfillment of these needs results in growth.

Observation of infants and children, shows us that, at the start of life, a person feels himself to be at one with the universe. He is in a kind of continuum with his environment since he feels omnipotent. Objects are as yet unclear and separate from himself. When others are preceived, they are seen only for what they give, not for what they need or require. Simultaneously, with this omnipotence and selfishness, an infant feels hungry, helpless, and in need of support in the form of food, warmth, and protection. Spurred by these survival needs, his appetite tends to be insatiable and often requires the control of people who love him to prevent him from getting into trouble by trying to incorporate too much. When frustrated or denied in his needs for support, he feels anger and fear of destruction rather than depression because he as yet has no conscience or sense of guilt. He tends to hurt himself rather than to lash out and fight others to dissipate his anger, tension, and fear. This tendency to self-injury, regularly arises in states of anger or frustration in dependent people and is symptomatic of this personality type.

In later life love, for the dependent person, is more a parent-child relationship than an interdependent one of equals, where each has some feeling of independence and security. Interdependent love is viewed by the dependent, immature person as dangerous. Jealousy is prominent in the love of dependent persons, since they feel empty, lack self-confidence, always want more, and see others as having more.

These mechanisms form the primary core of the dependent personality and exist in all of us in varying degree. While we may develop newer feelings and interests that are more realistic for our size and development, under stress we can easily regress back to this first position of life. Because of the feelings of emptiness and need and the inability to see the boundaries of the world of reality, the dependent person is in the unenviable position of feeling that he is the most important thing in the world, and at the same time, he is helpless and dependent for survival on the mercy and generosity of others whom he cannot fully appreciate. These feelings of selfish omnipotence on the one hand with helpless dependency on the other, unmitigated by sexual concern and aggravated by a tendency to self-injury under stress, lead to a bipolar situation in which the dependent person is both passive and aggressive at the same time. Because of the undeveloped ability to solve such contradictions, passive and aggressive drives remain unresolved and the individual feels dependent on parental people for survival.

THE DEPENDENT PERSON AT WORK

Transposing this dependent, passive-aggressive concept of one's self to the work situation, we begin to see an explanation of many common problems in work and understand why there is an inevitable struggle between management and labor. Passive-aggressive dynamics must inevitably involve balancing a desire for unlimited parental protection (often espoused by labor) against a strict, competitive, "laissez faire," "survival of the fittest" attitude championed by management. Labor's parental protection promotes dependency in the worker by centralization of power in the labor leader and manager with accompanying loss of individual initiative. Management's competitive attitude, in turn, fosters exploitation of the competitive struggle between individuals to the point where they tend to injure or kill each other rather than help each other. There is a gradual loss of appreciation that work is for *survival* rather than just to win an argument and gain individual supremacy. Both the desires for unlimited protection from aggression and for unlimited individual freedom to exercise it exist simultaneously in all of us, representing opposite poles of the dependency problem. These desires frequently lead to war and to destructive stalemates like strikes. They force one group to lead and one to be led.

Let us now examine in more detail the aspirations of each side of this duality of protection versus freedom so that we may better understand the conflict. *The passive worker* wants the approval and support of those in authority. He sees management as an unlimited source of supply, like Santa Claus. He can never be satisfied with the money and rewards that he gets, since his appetite is insatiable. Actually, these are not his primary objectives. Rather, he requires the security of good leadership and symbolic parental approval more than reward. He wants the safety of a job. He doesn't really know the value of money or how to use it wisely. In his condition of jealousy of and lack of concern for others and of fear of alliances, he has an insatiable appetite and a constant fear of death. The approval and guidance of his manager helps him to productive work and survival and will lead to his security and self-realization. Frustration of his dependency needs, that is, lack of security, approval, and the satisfaction of production more than lack of money, causes withdrawal more frequently than attack. The worker may feel sick, become accident prone or avoid the troublesome work situation by being absent, and seek parental help (symbolically) from his doctor. He may drink or abuse himself with medicine or threaten suicide in order to relieve his terrifying anxieties—anxieties about survival itself rather than about the lack of sexual satisfactions or money. His final and most important tool in relieving frustration will be some sort of passive sit-down strike in which he does not work, and by which he jeopardizes his own existence in his effort to handle his fear and anger.

The dependent manager is usually a person who shows more of the aggressive side of the passive-aggressive axis. He is a person who has repressed his feelings of emptiness and exaggerated his needs for omnipotence in an effort to hide his passivity. He is a man who needs to dominate and control and has an insatiable desire for money, position, and power, rather than for people, love, or creativity. He is more than ordinarily competitive and jealous. He squeezes others to get for himself. He frequently rejects his parents to hide his need for them and intensifies his self-image by consuming weaker people whom he scorns for their overt dependency. He wants freedom to carry on his aggression. He may lose his capacity for love in the struggle for power, which is so necessary to assuage his fear of being dependent and hurt by the environment.

Thus, we see the extremes of the seriously passive-dependent and the passive-aggressive as embodied in the worker-follower and the manager-leader. In between these extremes there exists every combination of the two postures. It should be mentioned that these people, living in constant anxiety about survival, are predisposed to tire easily under situational stress and develop "combat fatigue" that is manifested by feelings of tiredness, various physical complaints, chronic depression, paranoid feelings, difficulty sleeping, dreams of turmoil, and increasing inability to work.

We must study further the inherent contradictions that arise in managing the work area where passive-aggressive conflicts are prominent. Helping the dependent person by supplying protection in the form of more money for less work (gratifying Santa Claus fantasies) costs money, lowers production efficiency, and probably fosters more sickness, dependency, and loss of initiative. but might temporarily prevent a sit-down strike and self-injury. Curbing acquisitiveness threatens initiative, leadership, efficiency, but protects the individual and group unity. If an attempt is made to meet the worker's dependency needs in terms of security and money, there will be failure because these are insatiable and do not provide the security that comes when a person is helped to channel his energies into productive work that actually secures his survival in an indifferent environment. Raising salary and reducing work demands forces costs up and production down. Initiative disappears because there is no bite of cold reality to spur the individual on. In the resulting vacuum of helpless people trying to get something for nothing, power ends up in the hands of too few because the worker cannot accept individual responsibility and tends to pass it on to the one that promises him the most. Even so, protected people still get anxious because they have insufficient outlet for their energy. Protection alone is certainly not the answer to survival anxiety. Eventually, all of us have to face the reality of "survival of the fittest" and the fact is that for nothing you get nothing. If the "Santa Claus" need cannot be resolved, the individual ultimately ends in slavery or chaos.

On the other hand, if the selfish acquisitiveness of the severely passive-aggressive person is left unchecked, he too, as a manager, will never be satisfied and his efforts to get more will gradually force his oppressed slaves to revolt explosively. To deal with problems of balance between centralized power and individual responsibility to avoid the effects of misplaced dependency needs or narcissistic aggression, we must recognize that whoever attempts to reduce or interfere with individual responsibility and freedom is asking for group retaliation. At the same time when the competition inherent in individual responsibility ends, the slow deaths of private enterprise, individual initiative, and responsibility begin. Either the interests of the group are sacrificed to the narcissistic and insatiable struggle for omnipotence of a few or the immaturity and dependency of the group may plunge it into the hopeless chaos of people trying to get something for nothing. Either way ultimately leads to social decay.

SOLUTIONS

Fortunately, most of us tend to grow out of the first primative period of life with its anxiety for survival, insatiable appetites, and inherent contradictions. First, we learn to control and accept control, to sublimate our aggression in the productivity of work which brings satisfaction in the safety of environmental mastery. We become interested in reproduction as we master techniques of survival and our attention is gradually shifted by our biologically developing sexuality to love, which involves individual understanding, tolerance, and compromise. Both parties in a relationship, whether they champion protection or "survival of the fittest" realize that they are dependent on each other and cannot exist without each other. As a result they learn to curb their survival anxieties and compromise to accept each other's interdependent needs. Thus, productive work as a form of creativity and the ways of love provide the solutions to our survival anxieties. However, we can never totally escape them, and, in the work area, where interpersonal relations don't always seem essential to production we are particularly prone to revert to them.

While protectiveness and support may alleviate survival anxiety temporarily, they never cure it. The only cure lies in the productiveness of work. Narcissism and selfishness must be reduced. Anger and hostility must be turned to productive ends. While this is encouraged by parental generosity in protection, nutrition, and education, eventually, reality, physical growth, and frustration help the individual begin to produce for himself and help others. Because of the enormous hostility and selfishness associated with passive-dependent anxieties combined with limited capacities for self-concept and inhibition, there has to be some sort of authority and discipline for the growing child. This is best supplied by letting the older child "learn from experience" and reap the harvest of his own activities insofar as possible. He can be warned, protected, and educated to a point, but in the end he must face reality. For this reason, in group dynamics there is a great deal of safety in letting the individual alone and allowing "survival of the fittest" to operate between individuals and much danger in overprotecting them. Consequently, the conservative attitude, which often seems so harsh to the liberal is, in the long run, far kinder because once infancy is over it promotes survival far more efficiently than protection, which often plays into the Santa Claus fantasies.

Let us now examine some of the implications of these principles in the area of labor-management relationships. First, when management does not take into consideration the passive-aggressive dependency needs of workers and supervisors, a series of common problems begin to arise. Valuable employees quit, are ill, or not performing well because of lack of recognition, promotion or reward. There is lack of communication between groups in management and between management and the general working group that results in the crippling of individual security and in wasted efforts. Policies for handling incapacitated or incompetent people are ill-defined and inconclusive, increasing their incompetence and demoralizing others. There is poor evaluation and recording of employee's efficiency. Often there is overconcentration on the part of top management on technical details that allows insufficient time to develop major policy and procedure. The business or industry becomes unable to attract brilliant young men of high caliber. Incomplete recognition of work capacity often results in conscientious employees being pushed to the breaking point, or, in the reverse situation, in employees who feel that they do not have enough to do because no one watches them. There is insufficient recognition of the importance and impact of education and training.

We see that attitudes of the company, demands of the job, supervisory attitudes, and attitudes of fellow workers must all be considered in developing a healthful work environment. The worker cannot expect something for nothing. He cannot be given money for no work. This would never satisfy him. He wants help that leads to productivity and to self-respect, not the slavery of satisfying the symbolic parent to survive. Frequently, he cannot say what this help ought to be because he still tends to believe in Santa Claus. Good management must help him cope with his dependency problems by good rules that will result in happiness and productivity. This is the protectiveness that leads to maturity.

Good first-line supervision, fair administrative policy, in the light of these dependency mechanics, would demand that employees be treated as individuals as much as possible. It is wise to understand their life situations, both in and out of work. All efforts should be made to keep communications open. The supervisor must show the employee interest and respect. To do this he must be fair and honest. He must not baby the employee, but at the same time he must not expect an unreasonable amount of work. The supervisor should be as helpful as possible in getting the employee to expose his conflicts rather than to bottle them up. The supervisor must not go along with sick or unrealistic ideas on the part of the employee. Of particular importance is honest discussion of efficiency. If people are not doing well, they should be told so. The truth in the long run is always kinder than deception. If a man is going to improve, he should be told the truth so that he has the opportunity to meet his problem. It is never wise to hire or retain employees when they cannot basically do the job. Further, promotions and salary should be regulated primarily on the basis of productivity and efficiency, rather than longevity, seniority, or pity. Frequently, people with nervous disorders cannot be promoted or given increased responsibility at the same rate as fellow workers. If this is true, supervisors should not feel embarrassed about pointing out the problem and helping the employee to face it. Very frequently, these employees are quite happy not to be pushed beyond their abilities. By means of education, example, discipline, job jeopardy, or firing, good management often leads people to face emotional problems they have been avoiding. Neither management nor union should block realistic action when an employee really cannot perform.

In addition, we must consider the implication of dependency dynamics in the area of compensation. While all of us must be on the alert to temper aggression and competition to provide security for people who are not as strong as others, dependency can thus be fostered, and it becomes worthwhile for these people to be sick rather than to be well. They are particularly susceptible to this danger because of their handicap. Consequently, people should never be taken care of entirely. They must be allowed to suffer for their lack of application or inattention to the realities of life. Without frustration, no one can grow. Consequently, compensation and free care are extremely dangerous to mental health. It is against the laws of nature to supply something for nothing. Welfare can be as deadly as it is protective and supportive.

At the present time in our society we are facing a crisis in the concept of compensation awards for injury. Compensation insurance is making cripples out of thousands of people. There is no evidence in psychiatric literature that shows that compensation for injury promotes mental or physical health. On the contrary, its testimony shows the opposite. In our present social setup, we seem to be trying to place a monetary value on human life or the functioning part thereof. This seems to me to be most unhealthy. Money cannot replace life or function. Through the use of disability evaluation for compensation purposes, we make sickness valuable. This is totally unrealistic. We should be placing top value on health. Money should be spent to help people get well or maintain them while they are actually ill, but there is no good or realistic reason to award money for sickness or injury per se. Such money must be used to heal and rehabilitate. Injuries and illness are part of the natural risks of life. One does not deserve a reward for being injured or sick, but only help for getting well. The reward is health not money.

SUMMARY

To sum up, we see that industry exists for the survival of man, not simply for profit or its own end. The individual must constantly make sacrifices for the group, but on the other hand the group must never become overpowering for the individual. Leadership should be conceived of more as coordinating and stimulating than dictating and policing. Fundamental responsibilities and initiative should always remain with the individual even when this responsibility is heavy. The group must never take over this function. While individuals often need a lift, too much help may be worse than too little so that the best help is helping people help themselves, not direct giving or protecting. The strong will get further helping the weak, but not controlling them or deciding all things for them. Most happiness, freedom, productivity, probably come in a society or business that is so structured that people are not unduly protected from the damage that their unbridled selfishness, dependency, or need for power may procure for them. Maintenance of competition and decentralization seem the best methods to perpetuate this situation. Here no individual decides ultimately for others or controls absolutely. The individual has the opportunity to make or break himself. Both labor and management must constantly work to see that these principles are maintained in the occupational area. The worker must not become too concerned with getting something for nothing and the manager with the idea that profit is the only gauge of good business. Above all, we must always remember that work is fundamental to life and to mental health and that in most work conflicts each side is indispensable to the other.

V

Mental Health
Resources for
Industry

17 Vocational Rehabilitation

Ralph T. Collins

Stereotyped ideas of the nature of mental illness have seriously impaired the easy integration of the psychiatric casualty into the work force. Most laymen, understandably enough, have preconceptions about mental illness that prejudice them against associations with those who have or who have had a major mental illness. We are fearful of the unknown. We are apprehensive about people who develop illogical and bizarre behavior—who lose control. We are frequently reminded of the hostile and aggressive acts of the occasional patient who seriously disrupts his immediate environment.

With these concerns in mind, I asked Dr. Ralph Collins to discuss new programs that have allowed the successful and profitable employment of people who have had previous disabling psychiatric disorder. Further, I asked him to define for us the terms "sheltered workshop" and "half-way house" and to tell us how such facilities are now being used. Finally, I asked him: What is the likelihood of an applicant for employment with a history of psychiatric disorder having a subsequent disabling illness or becoming a threat to himself or others on the job?

Dr. Collins is uniquely well suited to respond to these questions. He has, since 1946, served as the consultant in neurology and psychiatry for the Eastman Kodak Company in Rochester,

New York. He also maintains an active general practice of psychiatry. A fully qualified specialist in both neurology and psychiatry, Dr. Collins is a 1932 graduate of the Albany Medical College, with subsequent specialty training at Columbia University, the University Hospitals in Iowa City, the Institute of Living in Hartford, Connecticut, and the Royal Edinburgh Hospital for Nervous and Mental Diseases in Scotland. Dr. Collins has served as chairman of the Committee on Occupational Psychiatry of the American Psychiatric Association, the Committee on Mental Health in Industry of the Group for the Advancement of Psychiatry, and the Joint Committee on Mental Health in Industry of the American Medical Association. Active in community mental health work, he has also been president of the New York State Association for Mental Health. Finally, to demonstrate the breadth of the man, he served as president of the Rochester, New York, Rotary Club in the late 1950's.

Vocational rehabilitation of the psychiatrically disabled person has improved greatly in the last two and a half decades. The 1943 Vocational Rehabilitation Act expanded the concept of rehabilitation to include provision of services to the mentally handicapped. The 1954 Vocational Rehabilitation Act further strengthened the law by providing more funds for research, for training rehabilitation counselors, and for grants to institutes for research in rehabilitation. In 1960, about three hundred rehabilitation research projects had been helped by these grants—twenty-seven of which dealt with the mentally ill. In the late 1940's the Veterans Administration pioneered the development of prevocational training and sheltered workshops within the walls of their psychiatric hospitals and began to interest local industries in taking their patients as employees.

The advent of the new psychiatric drugs improved the

condition of thousands of persons in and out of hospitals enabling them to resume their usual community living including their work. Newer attitudes of psychiatrists toward their hospital patients, including the well-known "open door" policy have allowed more patients to have freedom and develop confidence in themselves so that they are able to leave the hospitals earlier, returning to their communities and to their former jobs.

New facilities have been constructed. These include halfway houses, sheltered workshops, day and night hospitals, staging areas for community living, foster homes, and community mental health centers.

The President's Committee on Employment of the Physically Handicapped approved certain changes in its program of education and promotion in 1955 for the first time including the mentally restored and the mentally retarded. A subcommittee on Employment of the Mentally Handicapped was convened in 1959, and in 1963, the President's Committee decided to drop the word physically from the original title of the committee. The late President Kennedy effected this change through an Executive Order.

In 1963 the Federal Civil Service Commission made three significant changes in its rules for employing the mentally handicapped. The first stated that a person with a psychiatric history may take the Civil Service examination along with every other candidate for a job with the federal government. If the person passed the test and obtained a job, he was placed on a seven hundred-hour trial basis. If, after this trial, his work was satisfactory, he was to be placed on a permanent basis. Prior to this change, this same person would have had to have one year's satisfactory employment in civilian employment before he was allowed to take the test. Again, it was through the action of President Kennedy who issued an Executive Order to this effect in the fall of 1963 that this step was possible.

During the past five years, the President's Subcommittee on Employment of the Mentally Handicapped issued, *A Guide to Job Placement of the Mentally Restored,* a flier entitled, "So You're Going to Hire the Mentally Restored," the monthly *Newsletter* mentioning current data relative to the employment of the mentally restored and retarded, and a pamphlet entitled, "Wasted Assets," which encourages more grass roots programs to build a stronger bond between mental hospitals and the community. Public employment offices across the United States have also stepped up their efforts to find employment for the mentally restored.

In 1964 the Junior Chamber of Commerce adopted a policy calling for devotion of energies to obtain jobs for the mentally restored and to further research in mental retardation. Finally, the American Medical Association's Joint Committee on Mental Health In Industry published the manual: *A Guide to Employability After Psychiatric Illness.* This guide was for use by physicians in preemployment medical examinations.

Rehabilitation in today's mental hospitals includes psychiatric, social, and vocational emphasis. The last provides the patient with specialized services such as vocational counseling and guidance, training, development of work tolerance, specialized psychological testing, selective job placement, and vocational follow-up services. All phases of rehabilitation must mesh smoothly and purposefully in a common cause from the onset of treatment through discharge and follow-up services.

The Vocational Rehabilitation Administration (VRA) is a department of the Department of Health, Education and Welfare and it is currently administered by Miss Mary Switzer. Its duties are to enhance vocational rehabilitation through education, promotion, disbursing research grants, and overseeing vocational rehabilitation in the states. Each state administers its own local offices to train, retrain, and rehabilitate those who need help in getting a job or getting back on the job—the physically and mentally handicapped alike.

A psychiatric half-way house is a residential institution designed to meet the needs of an ex-mental patient during the difficult transition from the sheltered environment of the mental hospital to the more rigorous life of the community. Today, there are 75 half-way houses in the United States. Three criteria define a half-way house: (1) the residents have recognized psychiatric problems, (2) the house is not on hospital grounds, and (3) it is only the temporary residence of persons living there.

A sheltered workshop is usually defined as a workshop where patients learn or relearn skills, habits, and attitudes necessary for return to work.

In 1965 14,000 mentally restored persons were rehabilitated through various federal and state programs—three times the number five years before and seven times the number rehabilitated ten years previously. In that year, the mentally restored accounted for 12 percent of all handicapped persons rehabilitated; five years ago, only 6 percent; ten years ago, a mere 3 percent. Nine out of ten mentally restored persons had no earnings at the time they started vocational rehabilitation. Eight out of ten had become wage-earners by the time they had completed vocational rehabilitation.[1] Vocational counselors now are on duty in almost every mental hospital in the United States giving psychiatric patients an early start on the road to independence.

[1] Ralph T. Collins, "The Mentally Restored: An Unfinished Revolution," *Employment Service Review,* September 1966.

The Vocational Rehabilitation Administration has recently established psychiatric training centers for vocational rehabilitation counselors at the departments of psychiatry at Harvard and the Universities of Nebraska and Oregon. These counselors, who have been previously working with the physically handicapped toward vocational rehabilitation, spend six months at these centers learning the fundamentals necessary for them to return to their jobs prepared to work with the mentally restored toward vocational rehabilitation.

The June 1966 *Newsletter* of the President's Committee on Employment of the Mentally Handicapped describes a program at the VA mental hospital in Coatsville, Pennsylvania. Actually, there are four programs tying the hospital closer to the business community and resulting in more jobs for the mentally restored. (1) Employer—applicant clinics provide an opportunity for employer groups to visit the hospital each month to give tips on jobs to patients about to be discharged, to train patients on how to conduct themselves during job interviews, and to inform the hospital staff about the current job market. (2) Vocational planning clinics are held on a regular basis when members of the Coatsville Junior Chamber of Commerce come to the hospital to chat with patients and to give them job hunting advice based on their own work experiences. This program for younger men supplements the employer-applicant clinics. (3) Other business groups are invited to tour the hospital to see what is being done to prepare patients for employment. They gain a realistic view of mental illness and of the capabilities of the mentally restored. (4) Sheltered workshops give needed work experience to patients and serve local businessmen by demonstrating the job potentials of patients. The success of all these programs, the hospital noted, depends on close cooperation by vocational rehabilitation, employment service and hospital staff.

The *Newsletter* of the President's Committee dated April 1966 headlines another article entitled, "Preparation Makes the Difference." "Never absent, reliable, I'd never have known he was in a mental hospital. Fewer problems than with others." That's what employers are saying about ex-mental patients from the Brecksville VA Hospital near Cleveland, Ohio. The reason is a four step program of preparation, namely; (1) patient preparation, (2) employer preparation, (3) job interview, and (4) teamwork. The key man in the program of teamwork is the local veterans employment representative of the Ohio State Employment Service who spends much time at the hospital working with staff and patients.

While in recent years the employment opportunities of physically handicapped people have expanded considerably, comparable strides have not been made in the employment of former mental patients who still have a hard row to hoe in their attempt to find a place for themselves not only in the community but also in the economy. Progress in combating mental illness itself has been heartening, but logic suggests that it should be followed by an attempt to provide the social-industrial atmosphere necessary for helping the former patient become once again a useful member of society. In fact, there is now good evidence that an impressive number of chronically hospitalized patients can be successfully rehabilitated through gainful employment.[2]

Some remarkable results have already been obtained through a rehabilitation plan known as the Member-Employee program, which is now being conducted in forty Veterans Administration psychiatric hospitals. Briefly, it works as follows: when a patient reaches a certain level of recovery, he is hired by the hospital for a period of time lasting anywhere from three months to a year. He is paid a

---

[2] Josef E. Teplow and Reuben J. Margolin, "The Former Mental Patient: An Untapped Labor Source?" *Personnel,* January-February 1961.

salary and is expected to fulfill the same duties and responsibilities as any regular employee. Once the patient has attained satisfactory work performance, the supervisor in charge of the program, a VA counseling psychologist, finds him a job with an outside company. At this point liaison is established between the employing company and the hospital. The supervisor gives the employer a rundown on the skills and aptitudes of the member-employee (as the former patient is called), together with a brief history of his illness. Thereafter, the supervisor keeps in touch with the member-employee and the company on a regular basis, until the worker has been completely integrated into the community. In addition, the supervisor is always available to both of them for advice or consultation.

The Member-Employee program, or any program for restoring mental patients to the work community, has two basic requirements: (1) psychiatric treatment, followed by a realistic work-rehabilitation program in the hospital itself, and (2) a willingness on the part of industry to hire former patients and to follow the hospital's therapeutic recommendations for helping them adjust to their jobs.

Industry's reluctance to hire former mental patients, however, is to some extent justified: some companies have indeed suffered unfortunate experiences with these people. The blame, then, must be shared by the hospitals, which have sometimes discharged patients not yet fully rehabilitated or adjusted to normal working conditions. Naturally, every job failure reinforces the employers' stereotypes about mental patients.

It might be useful to look at some of the more common stereotypes: "I don't want my shop full of nuts." "Mental patients are offensive, unstable, assaultive, and not responsible for their actions." "I'm willing to hire a mental patient, but I'm afraid of the reaction of other employees." "Once a mental patient, always a mental patient. He can never be an effective worker again." "Mental patients are good only for unskilled jobs or, as some say, mental patients can't take pressure or accept responsibility." "This isn't my problem. Leave it to the doctors."

How do we break through these steroetypes? Is there anything you and your communities can do? To guide your thoughts, here are some examples of more action programs. In your community, for instance, what is the attitude and understanding of your physicians on this subject? Your clergymen, your social workers, your nurses, including the visiting nurses, your health officials, your city officials, your board of supervisors, your employers, your personnel people, your welfare agency, your school officials, your police officers?

In your community could this occur as it did in Akron, Ohio? Management, labor, DVR, psychiatric social workers, and psychiatrists interview once a month the about-to-be separated patients in the psychiatric hospital in that city about jobs.

In your community could this happen as it did in New Jersey? A gas station owner hired mentally retarded adults as attendants for one year. He then sent a letter with a few questions—explaining his experiment—to his regular customers and asking them for comments. They were satisfied.

In your community could this happen as it did in Baltimore and St. Louis? The Mental Health Associations helped discharged patients to brush up on office and clerical skills by having volunteers work with them. Job habits were especially watched such as grooming, being on time, ability to accept supervision, getting along with other employees, manners, telephone habits, caring for equipment, and being responsible.

In your community could this happen as it did in New

York City where a research unit studied some of the problems of the discharged patient? The first fifty patients studied gave information that showed that 40 percent of them found jobs on their own, 10 percent (women) returned as homemakers, 32 percent needed rehabilitation services, 6 percent were deemed unemployable, and 4 percent were rehospitalized.

In your community could this happen as it did in Vermont where the DVR, the state hospital, and discharged schizophrenic patients worked closely together in a half-way house with oustandingly good results?

In your community could this happen as it did in South Carolina where three programs known as PREP, STEP, and COPE were instituted in a rehabilitation program of psychiatric patients? PREP stands for Psychiatric Rehabilitation Evaluation Program. STEP stands for Skill training, Trial placement, Evaluation, and Preparation for release. COPE stands for Counseling, Occupational Training, Placement, and Evaluation. Fifty staff members of the hospital worked with these patients.

Dr. Reuben Margolin puts it this way:

> When an ex-mental patient gets a job, there are many ways in which he is reminded of his former patient status. His every action is watched and interpreted in light of his former illness. Oversolicitousness, morbid curiosity or anxiety on the part of employers can be obstacles barring ex-patients from the mainstream of life.
>
> Despite these roadblocks to adjustment, I am of the firm opinion that an individual should not conceal the fact that he has been mentally ill.
>
> Should we help mental patients seek jobs, or should they look for themselves? Most therapists think that the independence drive would be thwarted if patients were helped in their job-seeking efforts. I disagree. Many a patient who looks for

job opportunities by himself ruins his own chances. He would be better off if someone went along with him.

We have been greatly successful in getting patients out of the hospital, but we sputter badly in our efforts to keep them out. What's needed is follow-up. Regular follow-up visits for a designated period after discharge, plus follow-up provisions for dealing with crises should they occur, benefit not only patients but employers as well.

Many employers would be willing to give ex-patients a job, but fear prevents them from doing so. Assurance of regular follow-up would alleviate their anxiety.[3]

Employer attitudes toward employment vary from skepticism to enthusiasm. The chief obstacles seem to be fear, lack of knowledge, bias, and prejudice. It has been shown many times that when a mentally restored person has been adequately trained or retrained and prepared for employment by the psychiatrist, the vocational rehabilitation counselor, the psychiatric social worker, and then has been properly introduced to the new employer by the employment agency representative, a successful job placement usually results. The way is usually prepared by the employment agency representative. We have found that the first successful placement is all that is necessary to break the ice, and so that first placement is a critical one. I stress again that only those persons who are ready for work should work. We realize that business and industry are not rehabilitation agencies and that the name of the game is still profit.

Lane Bryant store on Fifth Avenue pioneered in this area when a few years ago its management decided to hire women who had been recently discharged from a mental hospital and who had been certified as being ready for work. The only restriction was that those women could work for

---

[3] *Newsletter: President's Committee of the Mentally Handicapped,* October 1963. Statements quoted from Reuben J. Margolin, M.D.

only 90 days for Lane Bryant. After this period, they would have to seek employment elsewhere. The reason for this stipulation was that the women would then have a "satisfactory work record" to get the next job. Lane Bryant regretted the day that they had made this rule, because they found many women they would have liked to have kept as employees.

More companies each year are covering mental illnesses in their major medical insurance plans—for both in-hospital and office visits. To define terms and provide possible standards for such coverage the American Psychiatric Association recently published *APA Guidelines for Psychiatric Services Covered Under Health Insurance Plans.*"[4]

Relapses do occur in persons with a psychiatric illness as they do with nonpsychiatric illnesses. The cardiac employee often has to reenter the hospital again; so might the diabetic. It is my personal experience at Kodak, and that of my colleagues, that these persons are excellent workers in spite of their relapses.

The continuing battle against prejudice and misunderstanding will not be easy. The roots of prejudice run deep. They do not give way easily. Too often the defense weapon is a "Yes, but . . ." The key in the treatment of mental illness very often is employment, a job, a chance to hold one's head up, and be beholden to no one.

Many employers have established written policy statements in favor of employment of the physically handicapped and the mentally retarded. Such policy statements regarding the mentally restored are nearly nonexistent. They could help a great deal in opening new doors for the mentally restored. The future does look bright. Acceptance of the mentally restored is coming, although slowly. The day is also

---

[4] American Psychiatric Association, *APA Guidelines for Psychiatric Services Covered under Health Insurance Plans* (Washington, D. C.: The Association, April 1966).

coming when mental illness will be looked upon in its proper perspective—as an illness that can be treated. The day is coming when the mentally restored will no longer carry the brand of "apartheid." They will be accepted as human beings, as productive and wanted members of our society. You and I must be convinced in our own minds that the mentally restored are deserving of full and equal opportunities to partake of the blessings of America. Once we are convinced, we must convince others. As Nicholas J. Oganovik said, "It's our thinking that's handicapped."

18 Resources in the Private Sector

John P. Lambert

Most Americans who develop a mental disorder obtain treatment privately. They see their family physician or internist and often are referred to a psychiatrist. To be sure, if hospitalization is required, it is as apt to take place in a state hospital as in a general hospital or private psychiatric hospital. But the primary resource is in the private sector. I therefore asked John P. Lambert, chairman of the Committee on Private Practice in Psychiatry of the American Psychiatric Association, to contribute this chapter on the private resources available to the employer.

Dr. Lambert received his B.S. from Princeton in 1931; his medical degree from Columbia University's College of Physicians and Surgeons in 1935. He completed postgraduate training in pediatrics, neurology and psychiatry at Columbia Presbyterian Medical Center and Johns Hopkins Hospital. He is a Diplomate of the American Board of Neurology and Psychiatry and associate clinical professor in Psychiatry at Columbia University. His principal professional role is medical director of Four Winds Hospital—a private psychiatric hospital in Katonah, New York. Formerly president of the Psychiatric Society of Westchester County, he is now a member of the Westchester County Community Mental

*Health Board. He is also chairman of the Standards Committee
of the National Association of Private Psychiatric Hospitals. In
addition to managing his hospital, he has served on the Board of
Directors of the Jekyll Island Packing Company and the Sea
Harvest Company and, in addition, is a member of the Advisory
Board of the County Trust Company.*

*I asked Dr. Lambert to tell us what an employer can do when
an employee develops an incapacitating mental disorder. What
private resources can he enlist? What about hospitals? Psychiatrists? Psychologists? Family physicians? In addition, what resources from the private practitioner can be brought to bear in an
industrial setting in advance of an acute psychiatric disturbance?
In other words, what preventive measures are available from the
private sector that can be used by the employer?*

Characteristic of the American community is the banding
together of people into clubs, organizations, and associations
to work in the area of health, education, and welfare. There
are many actual and potential resources in every community
able to provide mental health services to industry. These
services, although interrelated, can be thought of as: (*a*) diagnostic, (*b*) treatment, (*c*) rehabilitation, (*d*) prevention,
(*e*) education, and (*f*) research. The purpose of this chapter is to outline some of these, with particular attention to
the role of the psychiatrist in private practice who can provide both direct and indirect mental health services to
industry. I want to consider the manner in which industry
can recognize the need to utilize these resources and discuss
the impact industry can have on the field of mental illness
and mental health.

Mental health services are provided by various individuals
and organizations under private, voluntary, or governmental
sponsorship, functioning at the local, state, regional, and na-

tional level through a wide spectrum of programs and facilities. Organizations such as the National Association for Mental Health, The Family Service Agency, The American Red Cross, and religious groups are in operation in almost every community. A primary local resource in most communities is that of the private sector of the medical profession. In many areas local physicians have provided industry with emergency, surgical, and medical services. A number of physicians have developed a close working relationship with industry on a part-time, full-time, or consulting basis. They are a potential resource for mental health services. Some, and there should be more, have integrated psychiatric principles into their everyday practice of medicine,[1] and play an invaluable role in dealing with minor emotional disturbances. Psychiatrists are physicians who specialize in the diagnosis and treatment of emotional illness.

At the present time there are only six thousand psychiatrists in private practice in the United States. While they are still concentrated to a large extent in the major metropolitan areas of the country an increasing number are moving into the smaller communities. In conjunction with specialists from other disciplines, psychiatrists have developed programs and facilities for the treatment of the mentally ill and, in general, for mental health. Although comprehensiveness, quality, and quantity of available service may differ from one community to another, the net result is that more of these services have become available to a larger number of communities. If a particular service is not available in one area it can usually be found in a nearby community.

In the United States there are some one hundred seventy-five private mental hospitals.[2] Staffed by psychiatrists, psy-

---

[1] Group for Advancement of Psychiatry, "Medical Practice and Psychiatry: The Impact of Changing Demands," *Report # 58*, New York, N.Y., 1964.

[2] *National Association Private Psychiatric Hospitals, Directory*, Leonia, New Jersey.

chologists, and social workers, most of them provide a wide range of services beyond a direct treatment process and are increasingly involved in community services. A psychiatric service or unit in community hospitals is a recent but rapidly growing resource throughout the country. A future resource will be a national network of Community Mental Health Centers. As Dr. Yolles reported in chapter 4, some have been established already and do provide comprehensive services.

There has been a marked shift in the past few years in the private psychiatrist's focus and activities away from the hospital and office into the community. Changing concepts and techniques prompt him to move into the live-a-day environment of people, where he can intervene earlier before emotional disturbances become emotional disabilities. There has been a shift in the traditional role of therapist dealing with the mentally ill, namely diagnosis and treatment, to one in which he is involved with groups and organizations whose interests are in prevention, rehabilitation, education, and research. There are a number of psychiatrists who are not only aware of the impact on people of changing socioeconomic and cultural forces, but are interested in active participation with others, to guide and shape such forces for maximum benefit. A few psychiatrists in private practice have demonstrated interest in becoming better acquainted with industry, its policies, and functions. Some, however, have become actively involved with industry as occupational psychiatrists. These individuals have assumed leadership both in industry and in their profession by sharing their experiences and by stimulating a working relationship in both fields. Some have established the Center for Occupational Mental Health to disseminate information.

For many years psychiatrists in private practice and private psychiatric hospitals have been utilized by industry's employees and their families (over 400,000 patients in

1965).[3] Working with these patients as well as through knowledge from literature and professional meetings, psychiatrists, and other mental health workers (social workers, psychologists) have become aware of many factors in the work environment, as well as in the individual and his family, that influence the employee's capacity to adjust, adapt, and perform. In addition, the experience gained from extensive studies of the organization and operation of private psychiatric hospitals has led to the development of a number of important principles and concepts. These involve creativity, decision-making, interpersonal conflicts, the therapeutic community, and closely parallel observations cited by Myers (pp. 82-102). Out of such experience psychiatrists have developed knowledge that can be applicable in industry, provided it is used by management towards sustaining employee mental health.[4]

The psychiatrist functions in a variety of roles in supporting the mental health of industry's employees,[5] but in each the nature and extent of his responsibility must be clearly delineated. He may be a *therapist* to whom a patient is referred, a *clinical consultant* to the company's medical department, or a *consultant to management,* where he is involved in policy matters that affect the emotional climate of the organization. Additional contributions may be made as a participant in programs of research. Implicit in all his roles is an opportunity to contribute to the understanding of the dynamics of behavior in the work setting.

Although few business organizations have demonstrated any great sophistication or knowledge about the outward

[3] American Psychiatric Association "Survey of Private Practice," Biometrics Division, National Institute of Mental Health and Committee on Private Practice.

[4] Group for the Advancement of Psychiatry, "The Application of Psychiatry to Industry," Report No. 20, New York, N.Y., 1951.

[5] "Industrialization and Mental Health," Proceedings of 17th Annual Meeting, World Federation for Mental Health, Geneva, Switzerland, 1965.

manifestations of emotional disturbances in the work setting, many companies do vaguely recognize the need for such knowledge. It is unfortunate that the majority of industrial employers have not yet reached the point of awareness that there is something which they should but do not know in the area of mental health.[6]

Most of us can recognize the individual who shows mental illness that is characterized by a clear-cut disturbance in thinking, feeling, or behavior. People with such illness are usually referred to a psychiatrist without delay. Less evident, but much more important, are the manifestations of an incipient mental illness that can and should be recognized by management so that appropriate supportive measures may be taken either within the organization or within the community. There are many stresses and strains in any business organization to which employees may react in ways that may be destructive, not only to themselves but to the company. Research, by industry, has identified some of the factors that influence the capacity of the employee to adapt and perform. There is still a great need for further inquiry into those factors that support mental health, foster creativity, and enhance satisfaction in the work experience.

It is vital for industry, with its increasing sense of social responsibility as well as for its own economic interests, to identify not only its mental health needs but the resources to meet them effectively and appropriately. Therefore, a first responsibility of industry is to become familiar with the mental health resources in its community and to help such resources to become acquainted with the industry before any acute need for such services arises. A corporation should assign this responsibility to one of its staff members. Ordinarily this function should be given to a member of the med-

[6] Alan McLean and Graham Taylor, *Mental Health In Industry* (New York: McGraw-Hill, 1958).

ical department. It may be assumed that a physician in a company medical department is the best person to establish a relationship with psychiatrists in his community in private practice. In smaller companies the only medical service may be a full- or part-time nurse. In such cases it may be preferable to assign the responsibility for collecting information to the personnel director or to a member of top management, who will find the local medical society a readily available source. Many times, however, the nurse is well qualified for this role. The local Mental Health Association is frequently aware of psychiatrists interested in industry and who might be available for diagnostic evaluation of employees with emotional disturbances. A good deal of general and specific information can also be obtained from the national organizations or their local branches to which most professional mental health workers belong. These include the District Branches of the American Psychiatric Association and particularly the Committee on Occupational Psychiatry, those of the American Psychological Association, The National Association of Social Workers, and the National Association of Private Psychiatric Hospitals.

In communities where none of the above organizations have local members a local Council of Social Agencies may provide useful information. In some parts of the country, county or city Mental Health Departments are aware of psychiatrists who have shown an interest in or could be stimulated to devote time to industry.

A first and perhaps informal, contact with such a psychiatrist could be utilized to explore the general needs of the corporation, as well as the existing or potential interest of the physician. A luncheon invitation, for example, provides an informal means of questioning the physician about various resources and services which should be explored before establishing any firm relationship. Subsequent meetings may serve as part of a learning process for both parties. As the corporation executive learns of the areas and the ways in which the psychiatrist can be helpful, the physician in turn, will become better equipped in his knowledge of the corporation's philosophies. Only as the psychiatrist comes to know the corporation can his help be effective for both the employee and management. A number of psychiatrists in private practice have become involved in an industrial setting because former patients, now in upper management, recall the help they received themselves. When this occurs it helps dispel outmoded, yet prevalent, concepts about mental illness too frequently held both by workers and management.

As the private practitioner and the company develop a working relationship, the psychiatrist may be called on for help in an immediate and obvious situation—namely, the diagnostic evaluation and disposition of an emotionally disabled employee. If there has been some anticipation of such a crisis (all larger plants will experience these situations sooner or later) the employer may be better prepared to deal constructively with the situation. It is imperative that the employer, or a member of the administrative staff, face the situation directly. They should not attempt to avoid this type problem by finding some legal loophole to sanction the employee's discharge without consideration of his ultimate health. Attempts at "quick and easy" severance usually result in a "flypaper" situation. The more they struggle the stickier it will become. Many implications both obvious and subtle can be seen in the following example:

The wife of a forty-year-old middle management executive was called by one of his assistants and informed that one of the firm's executives thought her husband should see a doctor because he appeared emotionally upset and tearful. A psychiatric consultation revealed an acute depressive reaction with paranoid features and considerable suicidal risk so that hospitalization was necessary. The psychiatrist contacted the medical department of the corporation for information and was advised that the employee would be carried on sick leave until he recovered and then be told that he was terminated. It was only after much discussion that the company reluctantly communicated its decision directly to the hospitalized employee. This evoked many changes in the patient's thinking, feeling and behavior. He was able to leave the hospital in a matter of a few days with a clear realization of what had precipitated his emotional upset. The essential factors can be summarized in the following way: the patient, a high school graduate, had risen from route salesman to regional manager in charge of promotion. He was reassigned to direct a research and development activity directing unit composed of persons with advanced technical degrees. In this role he felt inadequate but was supported and encouraged by the vice president in charge of the division. The vice president retired some months before the patient was hospitalized. Following a brief period of rehabilitation this man was employed by another corporation who, at his request, contacted the hospital for advice as to his assignment. Currently he is holding a more important executive position than the one that he lost.

The referral of an employee for psychiatric treatment should not end the company's responsibility toward him. Management must recognize that emotional illness can be treated and that the occurrence of an acute emotional illness does not imply the individual will subsequently be incapable of carrying out his responsibilities to the fullest degree. The employment and orientation of a worker in industry is becoming an increasingly significant expense. To drop a worker because he has had an emotional illness and go through the process of employing a new worker is always expensive and often risky. Even in terms of cold economics, industry is better off going to considerable lengths to retain an experienced employee than to hire and train a new one. It must also be recognized that an emotional illness may have demonstrated the unsuitability of a person for *specific* duties and that continued successful functioning of such an employee can be, at least in part, dependent on the type of assignment given him.

It may be necessary in some cases, for a worker who has suffered an emotional disturbance to go through a rehabilitation process either in a facility designed for this purpose or perhaps in the plant itself. It may be desirable in some cases to adjust the working hours, temporarily change his assignment, or establish a particular relationship with someone in the medical department or with someone in management in addition to the person's own immediate supervisor. A change in work location, for example, may have a valuable rehabilitative effect on the employee. With adequate psychiatric consultation management can derive greater insight into the needs of their employees and determine the extent to which these needs can be realistically met.

It is obvious that providing some type of in-plant follow-up of the psychiatrist's recommendations is a necessity. In this manner the reoccurrence of those factors which precipitated the employee's difficulties may be avoided. If the employer considers such a worker useless, he not only hurts that individual unfairly, but may cause an unjustified and significant loss to the corporation. It is quite natural that an emotional outbreak in an employee affects his fellows. They may be concerned about the situation and want to help him. They may feel that the working conditions or job requirements were the cause of the emotional breakdown. They may pin this responsibility on a particular supervisor or may point to corporation policies as the cause. The action of management may be motivated entirely by a desire to help the sick person, but in doing so, they may involve the corporation in legal responsibility for the illness. The question whether this is a work-caused injury and subject to Workmen's Compensation immediately arises. What is the responsibility of the corporation to the psychiatrist to whom the patient may be sent, and what is the relationship and responsibility of the psychiatrist to the corporation which may be paying his bill, or to which he may be functioning as a consultant or in some other capacity?

None of these problems has simple solutions, but they will be faced more easily and solved more satisfactorily if planning to meet them is carried out calmly in advance, rather than under pressure at a time of crisis. If not already done, consideration should be given to planning for the economic threat that an illness may pose to the employee and the company. The manner and extent of financial support is not only a factor in prevention but can influence the treatment and rehabilitation of the emotionally ill person. Medical and surgical benefits to an employee and his family through insurance are well established. Insurance coverage for psychiatric hospitalization has so far been more limited. There is also the need to expand and broaden existing insurance benefits to provide for prevention and rehabilitation. Such coverage has been included in some union contracts. I expect greater emphasis will be placed on such programs in the future.

To help prevent emotional illness there must be an awareness of those situations inherent in industry which may precipitate emotional disturbances among some employees. The recognition of stress situations and the effect they may have on a particular type of personality is specifically an area in which the psychiatrist can make a significant contribution. An important function of some consultant psychiatrists is to conduct training programs which help sensitize management on various levels to greater understanding of human behavior, and therefore of emotional problems which may arise in daily work activity. Moreover, such training helps them recognize the potential implications of proposed changes in industrial processes or in staffing structure. The transfer to a different department, the appointment of a new supervisor, a change in working hours, or the introduction of new and previously unknown machinery create situations threatening the emotional stability of a worker, especially when he has a variety of problems in his home or social life. A proposed merger affecting the corporation, the introduction of a new and untried product, the organization of a new department, or increased responsibility or authority may just as easily threaten the corporation executive.

The private psychiatrist may be invited to join staff conferences at various levels of management. In this capacity he can help the participants to understand the difficulties which may exist in communication, resulting in misunderstandings and the development of problem situations. He can help them understand the bases for some of the disruptive kinds of behavior that can take place in an industrial plant or office by helping them understand the reasons for this behavior. He can aid in developing plans to avoid, so far as possible, those factors which contribute to crisis. Serving as consultant, the psychiatrist can help management in developing policies with regard to the selection of personnel. However, it is not suggested that he be directly involved in the actual selection of the employee since this is clearly a function of management. Assisting the personnel director in understanding various emotional situations that can be anticipated or aggravated by specific activities, and the type of personality which is most suited for a particular type of work, the psychiatrist can help develop a philosophy and clarify concepts of human interrelationships on which personnel policies can be established.

The psychiatrist can also often help management understand the implications of specific symptoms of potential disturbance. Chronic absenteeism is often due to specific physical cause, but it is at least as likely that it is due to emotional difficulties related either to the work situation or to a home situation, without the worker perhaps even being fully conscious of the cause.

While alcoholism in itself is obviously disruptive to sound working habits and clearly costly to any employer, it very often is symptomatic of a serious underlying emotional disturbance. Some corporations have found it economically as well as socially desirable to develop special programs to combat and to treat alcoholic workers. These programs often involve long periods of work with the employee and at times with members of his family.

A great deal of work has been done on the significance of accident proneness. There is an increasing body of knowledge that repeated accidents are not really "accidental," but are an indication of an emotional disorder in the victim.

An abnormal reaction to changes in procedures or to a reassignment on the job must be considered as indicative of an underlying, though possibly unrecognized, emotional problem. An excessive number of complaints, or a feeling by the worker that he is being "picked on" is a similar warning of an underlying problem. In a midwestern plant, it was recently found that 100 percent of such complaints came from only 28 percent of the employees.

Every plant manager is aware of the extent to which these types of symptomatic behavior occur on the job. With the help of a consultant psychiatrist, it is more likely that he will not merely seek to deal with the symptoms, but will understand that the underlying causes must be recognized and handled if these problems are to be solved. Only when he is helped to learn what the precipitating factors in the plant might be, will it be possible to attack the causes, rather than the person manifesting the symptoms. Much of this lies close to the area of prevention of mental illness.

SUMMARY

The psychiatrist in private practice in his diagnostic evaluation and treatment supervision of many patients employed in industry can be a vaulable resource in the mental health programs for industry. In collaboration with the psychologist and social worker the psychiatrist can function as a consultant assisting management and key personnel, to (1) identify stress and the maladaptive responses, and (2) develop programs and procedures to prevent them. The psychiatrist, as he develops knowledge through personal experience with an organization, can be a consultant to top management, advising on policy matters that influence the emotional climate of the organization. From industry the psychiatrist can in turn acquire a greater appreciation of the adaptability of the human being and the broad limits of that adaptability.

Industry is the most effective mental health resource in any community. Work in itself is the single largest force for mental health known to our society. All preparation or rehabilitation for living within our society is directed toward an eventual work experience. It is essential for each individual to have a satisfying involvement in his work. The organization and structure of industry in which so many persons are meaningfully involved affords both a laboratory and an "in vivo" experiment with unlimited research opportunity. Will industry recognize this unique opportunity? Will industry accept further responsibility and assume leadership in the field of mental health?

19 The National Association for Mental Health

Jeannette Rockefeller

For many years the National Association for Mental Health has been interested in promoting mental health services for industry. Its local and state chapters have sponsored literally hundreds of seminars for business leaders. While the resources of NAMH chapters vary considerably, most of them have resources which can and should be used by employers. Among others, an employer may learn about local facilities and may refer employees to the Mental Health Association. Occasionally rehabilitation services are undertaken as projects of MHA chapters. Under the leadership of Mrs. Winthrop Rockefeller, the NAMH has sharply increased its endeavors in the field of occupational mental health. For this reason, Mrs. Rockefeller was a natural choice to author this chapter.

Jeannette Rockefeller was elected president of the National Association for Mental Health after many years of service. Born and brought up in Seattle, Washington, she was raised to recognize community responsibility. In the mental health field, she began working as a trained volunteer with teen-age narcotic addicts at Riverside Hospital in New York. She also did case work for New York Infirmary's Social Service Department and worked

258

as a volunteer for the Psychiatric Clinic of the Court of Special Sessions of New York.

She has been instrumental in the development of the Arkansas Association for Mental Health and served as its president for three years. In addition to her interest in mental health, both Gov. and Mrs. Rockefeller have been active in the development of the Arkansas Arts Center, where she is president of the Board of Trustees.

In 1964 she was awarded the honorary degree of Doctor of Humanities by Arkansas College. In 1965 she received the International Fund Raising Association's Distinguished Service Award for her work in financing philanthropy. She was the first woman to receive this award.

In 1966, her husband was elected Governor of the State of Arkansas. It was during his campaign that Mrs. Rockefeller took time to prepare this discussion.

I asked Mrs. Rockefeller to describe the activities of NAMH and its component societies and to tell us something of other community and public resources available to the employer. I further asked: How can these be appropriately used by the occupational nurse, the industrial physician, personnel people, and line management? Do these agencies and does NAMH look to management and company professionals for support? How can better communications in support of employee mental health be brought about?

Great progress has been made in the past few years in developing plans for community-based mental health centers. These centers are to be cooperatively financed by the federal government, the state governments, and local communities; but the control will rest at the local level. The ambitious program launched by Public Law 88-164 is designed to erase the long-standing neglect of mental illness and mental retardation by providing a full range of treatment resources within reach of every community. If the federally initiated community mental health program is completely realized, there will eventually be help near at hand for every kind of mental problem.

Federal funds are now available for both the construction and the staffing of community mental health centers. Five "essential" services are to be furnished by these centers: outpatient care, inpatient care, partial hospitalization, emergency services, and consultation and education. It is understood that children as well as adults will be cared for, and that the services will comprise aftercare and rehabilitation as well as diagnosis and treatment.[1]

For the last two years, states have been making surveys and drafting plans that will enable them to take advantage of the "bold, new approach" to care of the mentally ill and mentally retarded. As of September 1966, all except eight states had received grants to help build community mental health centers; and staffing grants had been awarded to projects in twenty-two states, the District of Columbia, and Puerto Rico.

This planning process has involved many interested and concerned professionals and volunteers, as well as appropriate state and local government officials. By and large, however, the leaders of the business community—the industrial giants—have been conspicuous by their absence.

Assuming that a responsible business leader does want to do something about the mental health of his employees, to whom in the community can he turn for help? The answer to this question varies greatly from community to community.

---

[1] R. Glasscote, D. Sanders, H. M. Forstenzer, and A. R. Foley, *The Community Mental Health Center. An Analysis of Existing Models* (Washington, D.C.: American Psychiatric Association Joint Information Service, 1964); and *The Comprehensive Community Mental Health Center: Concept and Challenge,* Public Health Service Publication No. 1137 (Washington, D.C.: Superintendent of Documents, n.d.).

Because the mental patient for generations has been regarded as a ward of the state, not of the community, the development of treatment resources outside the realm of the state mental hospital has been haphazard. In some communities there is literally nothing in the way of a mental health facility. Disturbed persons who become a danger to others or to themselves are simply locked in a jail until they can be transferred to the nearest state hospital—which often isn't near. Even where resources are more or less adequate, those in need of care often aren't aware of their existence and don't know where to turn when a crisis develops.

A useful analogy is this: if a child breaks his arm, his parents almost always have a nearby hospital or a family doctor to rush him to; but, if this same child should suffer a severe emotional crisis, his parents probably wouldn't know whom to call or what to do. Recourse to the family doctor may sometimes be helpful; but, if intensive or extensive care is required, the family doctor may have no one to whom to refer the child. Many states have no special services or facilities at all for treating mentally ill children. They are placed in state mental institutions, sometimes on wards with adult patients; they are given no specific psychiatric treatment, and no effort is made to continue their education. In this day and age, such treatment seems a relic of the Middle Ages and shocking beyond belief.

THE MENTAL HEALTH ASSOCIATIONS

What does your community offer? At least it offers a local mental health association. The National Association for Mental Health, an organization of citizens seeking to improve care of the mentally ill, has more than nine hundred local chapters. One of these chapters is serving your community. In some parts of the country, the mental health association may be the only mental health service available and the only contact the state hospital has with the larger community.

How do we serve? Our program of action has four emphases, which I shall briefly outline.

First, we try to better the lot of the hospitalized mental patient. We are interested both in the patient and in the hospital in which he is confined. We assist the patient in a number of ways: by direct volunteer service on the hospital wards; by supplying patient needs in the way of clothing, cosmetics, reading material and games, and "luxury items," such as radios and television sets; by providing Christmas gifts for patients during the holidays; by helping relatives and friends visit patients, providing transportation for visitors to the hospital and for patients going home on brief leaves; and by serving as a connecting link between the hospital and the community, trying to help the patients keep in touch with the world outside the institution's walls.

Most important, we try, through legislative effort, to insure that sufficient state and local funds are appropriated to effectively run the institutions for the mentally ill. We are frank to admit that we are a long way from attaining nationwide success in this endeavor. The salary levels for professionals and aides working in most state institutions continue to be pitifully low, and the expenditure for the physical maintenance of patients, not to mention actual psychiatric care, is inadequate in most states. We have to keep fighting, insistently and persistently, for appropriations that will match the staggering dimensions of the problem itself. Federal pump-priming is essential, but the states and local governments have to shoulder their share of the financial as well as the administrative responsibility for caring for the mentally ill.

The second major concern of mental health associations is

better care for mentally ill children, within the community and in the public schools. The child who drops out of school because of emotional disturbance does not vanish from society. But society, up until now, has done very little to help this child.

In the last decade, the greatest increase in the incidence of mental illness has been among adolescents and preadolescents. This is of serious concern to us not only as parents, but also as responsible community leaders. The saying, "The future of our nation depends upon its youth," is trite but true. Major effort must be devoted to coping with mental illness among the young. This means special schools; teachers trained to deal with emotionally ill children; special treatment centers, including some residential facilities; and professionals specifically trained to help disturbed children. This has been one of the most neglected areas in mental illness, and we have just begun to realize that here is where we must begin, for the sake of prevention as well as cure. If we can recognize and check mental illness in children, then the toll among adults—among potential employees—won't be so great.

Our third program emphasis is the one most directly related to, and involved with, the business community. We seek to assist in the rehabilitation and the restoration of mental patients to community life. It is not enough to treat a patient, lead him to the point at which he can leave the hospital, then discharge him to a community that is perhaps hostile and that provides little or no aftercare or rehabilitation, and to employers who will not hire him because he has been mentally ill. The transition from institution to community is frightening and difficult for some former mental patients who need considerable help in making their way back to a semblance of normal existence.

A great deal needs to be done in educating potential employers to the fact that the former mental patient is not only hirable, but desirable, as an employee. Research studies[2] we have sponsored demonstrate that former mental patients are more appreciative of their jobs than the average employee, are less accident-prone, and are less apt to be absent from work than other employees. The former mental patient has shown that he, or she, is, in most cases, a conscientious and reliable worker. Unfortunately, not enough employers are aware of this.

Mental health associations continue to struggle against certain attitudes prevalent in some industries, which are expressed through unwarranted fears of former employees. Some application forms ask for instance, "Have you ever suffered from mental illness?" or, "Have you ever had a nervous breakdown?" While I have no objection to the use of such questions in a medical history form where this information is part of a doctor-patient relationship—even at the time of employment—including this kind of question in a routine employment questionnaire is reprehensible. In addition, many companies fail to provide employees insurance coverage for mental illness and, generally, demonstrate a lack of interest in the total problem.

Although progress has indeed been made in the past few years to change public attitudes, the average person often still rejects the former mental patient. The illness is frequently a source of embarrassment to members of the patient's family as well as to the patient himself. The tendency to regard mental illness as an unmentionable social disorder

[2] N. J. Cole, D. L. Brewer, and C. H. Hardin Branch, "Socio-Economic Adjustment of a Sample of Schizophrenic Patients," *American Journal of Psychiatry* 120 (November 1963):45; N. J. Cole, D. L. Brewer, R. B. Allison, and C. H. Hardin Branch, "Employment Characteristics of Discharged Schizophrenics," *Archives of General Psychiatry* 10 (March 1964): 314, and N. J. Cole, D. Covey, R. L. Kapsa, and C. H. Hardin Branch, "Employment and Mental Illness, *Mental Hygiene* 49 (April 1965):250.

is particularly common among blue-collar workers. This creates a special problem when it comes to rehabilitation of the former patient because, sometimes, an employer may place a former patient in a satisfactory job setting only to have the patient's fellow workers reject him, out of fear or misunderstanding. Mental health associations seek to educate both potential employers and employees, who must learn to accept the ex-patient in much the same way they would accept one who had recovered from a physical illness.

Our last major program emphasis is one to which I have already referred—the development of community resources for treating all kinds of mental disturbance at all levels of society. This is a program of utmost importance to the business community since the achievement of more sophisticated treatment methods and facilities could conceivably save billions of dollars by reducing the toll taken by America's most serious and prevalent health problem.

How can members of the business and industrial establishment profitably work with the local and national mental health associations? We should like to see them working with us both as citizen participating members and as clients. Let us look first at the client role.

Many mental health associations sponsor seminars and workshops for business and industrial executives. At such seminars, those who deal with personnel problems are made aware of the sources of tension in the working environment, the importance of human interrelationships in the everyday working situation, personality factors as causes of disturbance, and the influence of their own mental health on that of those working under them.

We all know that, in every place of work, the difficulties that are most troublesome have their roots in personalities, not in the technical aspects of the enterprise. All too often the "troublesome" employee is simply dismissed. Frequently no effort is made to find out why a particular person becomes persona non grata among his fellow workers, usually for reasons that he himself can't fathom. Rarely is an attempt made to help the person determine what emotional factors are causing the difficulties, and how he or she can cope with them and eventually contribute to a harmonious working environment. Mental health associations aim to increase the insight of those in positions of authority, so that people in trouble will encounter understanding, not rejection, on the part of those on whom they depend for a livelihood.

The seminars and workshops also try to increase employers' acceptance of the mentally ill, so that they will be less reluctant to give ex-patients a chance to get back into the mainstream of life. The emphasis on work in our society—based, at least in part, on the protestant ethic—makes it impossible for the ex-patient to be considered completely "restored" unless he is able to take his place in the working world. Management's attitude toward the mentally ill is therefore crucial to the successful rehabilitation of the mentally ill.

Another service that the mental health association renders to business and industry is supplying information on what is available at the local level for the care of the emotionally disturbed employee. Virtually every mental health chapter has an information service to assist the public in locating appropriate resources for care of the mentally ill. If a family, an employer, or a personnel counselor wants to know exactly what is at hand in the community in the way of treatment facilities and professional help, the local mental health association should be able to supply the answers. A number of our chapters publish directories of area treatment facilities and psychiatrists, psychologists, and other therapists in practice. Providing this type of free community information and referral service is among the most valued of mental health association activities.

The business executive needs to discover what is available in his community and what might need to be made available. He needs to be aware of possible sources of assistance that he might not normally think of when seeking help for people in trouble. For example, in recent years many clergymen of all denominations, have begun to take seriously, and to devote considerable study to, their duties as mental health counselors. A knowledgeable minister with adequate training in mental health counseling can be an effective participant in an employee mental health and education program. Other community agencies that offer assistance of many types are family counseling services, child guidance clinics, and public welfare services. People from social service agencies and psychologists and psychiatrists who are interested in community service can be recruited for programs for the benefit of employees.

A company is particularly fortunate if the area in which it is located has a medical school, for the relevant departments in such a school can furnish many qualified resource persons to help cope with employee problems and participate in employee educational programs.

You will note that I approach the development of mental health programs in industry from the viewpoint of total human relations, not from the limited focus of the employee and his job. It is not enough for industry to be concerned with the relationship of the employee to his job and to his fellow workers, ignoring the man who leaves the plant or office at 5:00 P.M. to take his place in home and community. It is obvious that a person carries his home-based problems to work with him and, conversely, carries his on-the-job problems home with him. Industrial mental health programs therefore have to have as their basic premise the promotion of the mental health of the *whole* man, not just the nine-to-five employee at his work!

Another potential limitation of industrial mental health programs is the adoption of a punitive approach rather than a constructive one. Certainly, the three "A's"—absenteeism, alcoholism, and accidents—are troublesome and frustrating to management. The alcoholic employee, however, is likely to try to overcome his addiction if he feels that the company is sympathetic and anxious to help him. Emphasis on helpfulness slants an industrial mental health program toward actual benefit to the employees and relieves them of the fear that management's recognition of emotional disturbance may cost them their employment.

Here is one of the areas in which the comprehensive, community-based mental health center may prove a real boon. If the wage-earner can be treated near home, perhaps on a part-time basis, he may be able to continue working to some extent, perhaps in a job requiring less of him than his ordinary occupation. But the cooperation of management will be vital in this case, for management must be willing to accept the man who is under treatment and try to place him in a spot suitable to his needs and current emotional condition.

Some small companies, particularly on the West Coast, have developed effective mental health programs with the aid and cooperation of the local mental health association and other community organizations and agencies. The goal of employee mental health and education programs should be to help workers understand themselves and their fellow men better, to teach them how to deal with their tensions and problems, to give them a greater sense of emotional security, and to aid them in gaining insights that can enhance their appreciation both of their job service and of their participation in home and community life.

To turn, finally, to business and industrial leaders as

members in our voluntary movement, we should like you to become really involved in what we are doing, to serve on our boards and committees, and to offer us guidance in the domains in which you are the experts. We, in turn, offer you all the help we have at our disposal. We can help you find and make effective use of the facilities in your area, and, with your aid, we can increase these facilities so that they will better serve the mentally ill.

Although ours is a voluntary citizens' organization that does not lay claim to any professional expertise, most of our divisions and chapters have a professional advisory committee. This committee is generally made up of top professionals from the community, representing all of the relevant disciplines plus the clergy. The function of the professional advisory committee is to give counsel on, and to supervise appropriate aspects of, the mental health association's community service program. Such a committee would usually welcome an opportunity to assist an interested business concern in developing a comprehensive employee mental health program.

Highest in "action priority" for industry leadership are the promotion of local comprehensive treatment centers and aid in the rehabilitation of former mental patients. Relevant to the latter is a quotation from Shakespeare:

Tis not enough to help the feeble up . . .
but to support him after, that's the worthy thing.

All of us have a big stake in the provision of better care for the mentally ill. Mental illness cannot be wiped out by halfway measures, half-hearted effort, and part-time interest. It is a massive problem, demanding the fullest and most dedicated kind of support from members of the business community. We look forward to increasing interest and effort on the part of business and industrial leaders in our fight against mental illness.

VI

Summary

20 The Future of Mental Health in Industry

Alan McLean

In examining the many faces of mental health and mental disorder of interest in the business community, this volume has emphasized mental illness. We have been made aware of the nature and extent of the influence of mental disorders in the industrial environment. Dr. O'Connor defined the challenge in both statistical and human terms. Chapters on rehabilitation and resources further spoke about this topic. The section on executive stress also emphasized emotional reactions to job pressures.

To properly summarize, we must look beyond the complexities of mental disorder. In the future, I suspect there will be more concern and greater demonstration of employer responsibility for encouraging mentally healthy behavior in employees with less worry about those with mental illness. It will be increasingly possible to identify work-related factors which act as triggers for disability and it will be possible to more accurately stimulate not just the avoidance of symptoms but healthy and productive reactions to the world of work.

emotional support have emerged. For many—particularly technical, managerial, and professional people—there is an increasing tendency to identify with the corporate employer. This suggests that, for them, it is the work organization that increasingly provides a thread of continuity for a family moving from one part of the country to another. It is the corporation that provides a way of life, including much of the necessary psychological sustenance. More than ever a man's social relationships are apt to arise from his work associations. For the hourly employee, work still has great meaning even though the patterns of identification vary more widely. For a few, the world of work remains an increasingly brief, distasteful interval in the sandwich of life. For most, however, I believe these observations are valid.

As people increasingly turn to work and to the employing organization for psychological and social gratification, other sources of satisfaction become less important. But there is a danger here. That danger is that they become more vulnerable to a life at work, since the employer literally holds the psychological and social support of the man and his family in his control. The employer's responsibility for utilizing his employees is enhanced. One can no longer simply discharge an individual whose skills have become obsolete without recognizing the psychological implications to the individual and to his family.

As you see, I am not inclined to believe in the doctrine of leisure time as a major threat to the mental health of present and future generations of workers. Even if we come to a four-day week, the psychological involvement with meaningful work will retain its importance. And to these idyllic four days, I suspect we will add increased commuting time, hobbies that are played out with the same intensity as work and a do-it-yourself society which changes only the locale of the work setting and the nature of the employer. This is to say nothing of further escalation in moonlighting activities.[1]

Against this frame of reference we are now in a position, theoretically at least, to draw upon the clinical and behavioral sciences in structuring job situations which will allow the employees at all levels in an organization to more fully develop their psychological, social, and cultural needs through the work environment. We are on the first step of a path that will lead toward increasing acceptance of the validity of psychological data in application to personnel policies of American industry. With this proposition in mind I would like to venture a series of predictions that seem both realistic and scientifically compatible with currently available knowledge and techniques. These may be the fall-out of appropriate concern on the part of the employer for mentally healthy behavior of his employees.

1. At least by the turn of the century, I suspect there will be more accurate, detailed systems of feedback of employee opinion and reaction and feeling about the work situation. Such a system will provide management with continuing, psychologically valid data concerning the *real* conscious and unconscious work-related needs of employees. This feedback will, in turn, suggest appropriate, realistic methods of satisfying these needs without fostering the excessive dependency and conformity which Dr. Meineker mentioned in his chapter on labor-management relations. With appropriate safeguards, these techniques need not be used to exploit or manipulate. Present-day surveys of job satisfaction, of morale and motivation, and of factors influencing employee mental health have already developed most of the necessary techniques.

2. We will have the capability for on-going, in-company

[1] The balance of this chapter is adapted from an article that originally appeared in the November 1962 issue of *Industrial Medicine and Surgery*.

research to direct company-employee communications more effectively. This will provide a flow of continuous, organized information to management concerning current employee feelings about the organization, the immediate boss, the job. Such input, based upon valid clinical and behavioral laws, will stimulate more prompt and adequate company communication to employees. In the process, we will be able to tap more accurately the less conscious processes of individuals, of work groups, and of the corporate personality, while at the same time meeting more clearly the unspoken needs of employees. The results could be a marked reduction in labor-management strife and an equal reduction in the stressfulness of the work situation.

3. There has always been a psychological contract—an unwritten set of rules—governing the relationship between the individual and his company. I suspect that in the future this contract will be more carefully spelled out and the roles implicit in the contract more appropriately fulfilled by management—by a management that need not be seduced into fostering excessive dependency of employees on the organization and which will clearly recognize that the employee who is treated as less than a fully mature, responsible adult will behave like one.

4. More than ever, management education in concepts drawn from the clinical and behavioral sciences will be effective in training business leaders to utilize the findings of the applied behavioral and clinical scientists. Such training may well consist of individual education—perhaps at times bordering on psychotherapy—in order that managers may learn to know themselves and to be aware of their own feelings in their daily practice of the profession of management.

5. Periodic medical examinations geared to the individual health needs of all employees will be far more commonplace

than they are today. Information available from these examinations will be ethically used in a sophisticated manner to insure not only initial but also continuing job placement in keeping with the individual's physical *and* emotional capabilities. Even more than today, medical, psychological, and social science ethics will obtain, insuring confidentiality and acceptance of these techniques by employer and employee alike. But the prime difference between current practice and that of the future is that such examinations will include evaluations of the emotional needs of individuals as a matter of routine.

In brief, some other predictions that should help foster mentally healthy behavior in the work place of the future: (1) A deliberate attempt will be made by sophisticated corporate managements to provide a wide variety of sources of gratification in each job. While fragmentation may be technically necessary, within the components of each position there will be a balanced variety of assignment. (2) Stereotyped patterns of rigid conformity to corporate direction of activities unrelated to the immediate job will disappear. Each employee will be allowed more latitude in the way he fulfills the needs of his job. He will be less frequently rewarded for off-the-job conformity and behavior. (3) Appraisal programs will become much more sophisticated. Without becoming amateur psychologists, managers should be in a better position to help employees develop their vocational potentials.

CONCLUSIONS

While this book has with a broad brush introduced some contemporary concepts from psychiatry, occupational medicine, psychology, and from voluntary and federal agencies, we have but scratched the surface. A dozen similar volumes would be necessary to properly exploit our present knowledge. Left untouched were the relationships between advancing technology and mental health. Nothing was said of the elusive human factor involved in the industrial accident. Management training came in for hardly a mention. Concepts of motivation and of behavior were largely omitted. Specific types of psychiatric disorder and personality disturbance were left for another time. Alcoholism as it affects the job was mentioned only in passing.

One final word: while I forecast significant change in the value system as well as in the operating procedures of industry and contend that they are inevitable, this should not bar any of us from giving the inevitable a little push. This volume has illustrated the contemporary challenge to American industry—and in so doing has suggested realistic techniques to tackle the task. The triangular affair of the clinician, the behavioral scientist, and the business leader is off to an encouraging start. As with all multilateral relations, there will be awkward times ahead. There may be interprofessional squabbles over appropriate role and task. And we can expect increasing governmental and union involvement. But in working through these relationships—in defining goals and responsibilities, the mental health of all of us in the work world will, hopefully, be enhanced.

Appendices, Bibliography, and Index

Appendix A

283

Appendix A

Director: ALAN McLEAN, M.D.
> *Psychiatric Consultant, International Business Machines Corporation*
>
> *Clinical Assistant Professor of Psychiatry, Cornell University Medical College*

Appendix B

C. J. BACKSTRAND
Chairman of the Board, Armstrong Cork Company

THOMAS J. BANNAN, Chairman
Western Gear Corporation

ELLIOTT V. BELL
Chairman, Executive Committee, McGraw-Hill Inc.

B. D. BILLMAN, Vice President
Armco Steel Corporation

H. GLENN BIXBY, President
Ex-Cell-O Corporation

WILLIAM T. BRADY
*Chairman, Advisory Committee of the Board, Corn Products
Company*

WILLIAM S. BREWSTER, President
United Shoe Machinery Corporation

EDWIN R. BRODEN
Chairman and President, SKF Industries, Inc.

JOHN BURKHART, President
College Life Insurance Company of America

WALKER L. CISLER, Chairman
The Detroit Edison Company

BERT S. CROSS, President
3M Company

GEORGE C. DELP, President
New Holland Machine Company

RUSSELL DeYOUNG
Chairman & Chief Executive Officer, Goodyear Tire & Rubber Company

B. R. DORSEY, President
Gulf Oil Corporation

E. J. DWYER, President
The Electric Storage Battery Company

HARMON S. EBERHARD, Director
Caterpillar Tractor Company

J. ROBERT FLUOR, President
The Fluor Corporation, Ltd.

R. G. FOLLIS
Chairman of the Board, Standard Oil Company of California

W. E. GORDON, Vice President
E. I. du Pont de Nemours & Company

P. A. GORMAN, President
Western Electric Company

JOHN D. HARPER, President
Aluminum Company of America

FRED L. HARTLEY, President
Union Oil Company of California

JACK K. HORTON, President
Southern California Edison Company

DONALD L. JORDAN
Chairman of the Board, Johnson-Carper Furniture Company, Inc.

W. W. KEELER
Chairman of the Executive Committee, Phillips Petroleum Company

JOSEPH B. LANTERMAN, President
Amsted Industries, Inc.

WILLIAM F. MAY
Chairman and Chief Executive Officer, American Can Company

CHARLES F. MOORE
President & Chairman of the Board, Diamond Crystal Salt Company

JAMES F. OATES, JR.
Chairman of the Board, The Equitable Life Assurance Society of U.S.

DANIEL PARKER
President & Chief Executive Officer, Parker Pen Company

WALTER F. PATENGE
President & General Manager, Wohlert Corporation
GUY S. PEPPIATT
Chairman of the Board, Federal-Mogul Corporation
PETER T. SINCLAIR, President
Crown Zellerbach Corporation
E. L. STEINIGER
Chairman of the Board, Sinclair Oil Corporation
HOWARD T. TELLEPSEN, President
Tellepsen Construction Company
GEORGE C. TEXTOR, President
Marine Midland Grace Trust Company of N.Y.
K. R. VAN TASSEL, President
A. B. Dick Company
LESLIE H. WARNER, President
General Telephone & Electronics Corporation
JOSEPH C. WILSON, Chairman
Xerox Corporation

Bibliography

American Psychiatric Association. "Troubled People on the Job." Committee on Occupational Psychiatry. The Association, Washington, D.C., 1959.

American Psychiatric Association. *The Mentally Ill Employee: His Treatment and Rehabilitation.* Committee on Occupational Psychiatry. Hoeber Medical Division, Harper & Row Publishers, 1965.

American Psychological Association. "The Psychologist in Industry." Division of Business Industry. The Association, Washington, D.C., 1959.

Anderson, V. V. *Psychiatry in Industry.* Harper, New York, 1929.

Argyris, C. "Organizational Effectiveness Under Stress." *Harvard Business Review* 38, No. 3 (May-June 1960).

Argyris, C. *Personality and Organization.* Harper, New York, 1957.

Barry, C. E. "Clinical Counseling—Its Value in Industry." *Personnel Journal* 42 No. 1 (January 1963):21-24.

Bartemeier, L. H. "Mental Health in Industry: Employer-Employee Relationships." *Bulletin of the World Federation of Mental Health* 2, No. 6 (1950):36-43.

Beard, J. H., Schmidt, J. R., and Smith, M. M. "The Use of Transitional Employment in the Rehabilitation of the Psychiatric Patient." *Journal of Nervous and Mental Diseases* 136 (May 1963): 507-514.

Behan, R. C., and Hirschfeld, A. H. "The Accident Process II. Toward More Rational Treatment of Industrial Injuries." *Journal of the American Medical Association* 186, No. 4 (October 26, 1963):300-306.

288

Bennis, W. G., Benne, K. D., and Chin, R. (editors). *The Planning of Change: Readings in the Applied Behavioral Sciences.* Holt, Rinehart & Winston, New York, 1961.

Bieliauskas, V. J., and Wolfe, H. E. "The Attitude of Industrial Employers Toward Hiring of Former State Mental Hospital Patients." *Journal of Clinical Psychology* 16 (1960):256-259.

Black, B. J. "Rehabilitation of Post Psychotic Patients by Industrial Workshop." *Diseases of the Nervous System* 22, Supplement 6 (April 1961):125-128.

Braceland, F. J. "Emotional Problems of Executives." *Michigan Business Review* 8, No. 2 (1956):1013.

Brown, J. A. C. *The Social Psychology of Industry, Human Relations in the Factory.* Penguin Books, Baltimore, Md., 1954.

Bureau of National Affairs. "Employee Counseling." The Bureau, Washington, D.C., Survey No. 63, 1961.

Burling, T. *You Can't Hire a Hand and Other Essays.* New York State School of Industrial and Labor Relations, Cornell University, Ithaca, N. Y., February 1950.

——. "Psychiatry in Industry." *Industrial Labor Relations Review* 8, No. 1 (1954):30-37.

Cameron, D. E., and Ross, H. G. *Human Behavior and its Relation to Industry.* McGill University, Montreal, Canada, 1944.

——. *Studies in Supervision.* McGill University, Montreal, Canada, 1945.

Caplan, G. "Concepts of Mental Health and Consultation." U.S. Government Printing Office, Washington, D.C., 1959.

Clark, R. E. "Psychoses, Income and Occupational Prestige." *American Journal of Sociology* 54 (March 1949): 433-440.

Collins, R. T. *A Manual of Neurology and Psychiatry in Occupational Medicine.* Grune & Stratton, New York, 1961.

Culpin, M., and Smith M. *The Nervous Temperament.* Government Publications—Medical Research Council, Industrial Health Research Board, Report No. 61, 1930, H. M. Stationery Office, London, England.

Dunn, J. P., and Cobb, S. "Frequency of Peptic Ulcer Among Executives, Craftsman and Foreman." *Journal of Occupational Medicine* 4 (July 1962):343-348.

Dunnette, M. D., and Bass, B. M. "Behavioral Scientists and Personnel Management." *Industrial Relations* 2 (1963):115-130.

Eliasberg, W. "A Study in the Psychodynamics of the Industrial Executive." *Journal of Clinical Psychopathology* 10 (1949):276-294.

Farnsworth, D. L. "Health Under Pressure." *Harvard Business Review,* November-December 1957.

Felix, R. H. "How a Businessman Stays Healthy." *Nation's Business,* September 1956.

Felton, J. S. "How to Stay Healthy Though Overworked." *Dun's Review* 72 (August 1958):42-43, 85-87.

Fortune. "The Alcoholic Executive." January 1960.

Fountain, C. W. "Labor's Place in an Industrial Mental Health Program." *Mental Hygiene* 29, No. 1 (January 1945):95.

Fraser, R. "The Incidence of Neurosis Among Factory Workers." Government Publications—Medical Research Council Reports, Industrial Health Research Board. H. M. Stationery Office, London, England, 1947.

French, J. R. P., Kahn, R. L., and Mann, F. C. (editors). "Work, Health and Satisfaction." *Journal of Social Issues* 28, No. 3 (July 1962).

Goldstein, D. H. "Motivations in Return to Work." *Industrial Medicine and Surgery* 30 (February 1961):64-65.

Grace, J. "Keep Your Employees Out of the Hospital." *Harvard Business Review* 37, No. 5 (1959):119-126.

Gravley, G. G. "Jobs and Emotions." *The Wall Street Journal,* page 1, March 5, 1963.

Greenblatt, M., and Simon, B. (editors). *Rehabilitation of the Mentally Ill.* American Association for the Advancement of Science, Washington, D.C., 1959.

Greenwald, H. "Psychoanalytic Profile of a Factory." *Psychoanalysis* 5, No. 4 (1957):27-37.

Group for the Advancement of Psychiatry, Committee on Psychiatry in Industry. "The Application of Psychiatry to Industry." Report No. 20, July 1951. (104 East 25th Street, New York, N.Y. 10010).

———. "Person with Epilepsy at Work." Report No. 36, February 1957. (104 East 25th Street, New York, N.Y. 10010).

Guest, R. *Organizational Change: The Effect of Successful Leadership.* The Dorsey Press, Homewood, Ill., 1962.

Gurin, G., Veroff, J., and Feld, S. *Americans View Their Mental Health. A Nationwide Interview Survey.* Basic Books, N.Y. 1960.

Hershey, R. "The Psychopathologies of Business Life." *Personnel Journal* 39 (1961):359-362.

Herzberg, F. *Mental Health in Industry.* Psychological Service of Pittsburgh, 1955.

Himler, L. E. "Occupational Rehabilitation Following Mental Illness." *Industrial Medicine and Surgery* 29 (October 1960):480-483.

Hirschfeld, A. H., and Behan, R. C. "The Accident Process. I. Etiological Considerations of Industrial Injuries." *Journal of the American Medical Association* 186, No. 3 (October 1963): 193-199.

Jaques, E. *The Changing Culture of a Factory.* Dryden Press, New York, 1952.

———. *Equitable Payment.* John Wiley & Sons, New York, 1961.

Kahn, R. L., Wolfe, D. M., Snoek, J. D., and Quinn, R. P. *Organizational Stress: Studies in Role Conflict and Ambiguity.* John Wiley & Sons, New York, 1964.

Knight, J. A., and Baird, V. C. "Mental Health in Industrial Practice. Mental Hygiene Among Employees." *Journal of Occupational Medicine* 3 (August 1961):365-368.

———. "Mental Health in Industrial Practice. Early Detection of Emotional Disorder." *Journal of Occupational Medicine* 3 (September 1961):412-416.

———. "Mental Health in Industrial Practice. The Part-Time Psychiatrist in Industry." *Journal of Occupational Medicine* 3 (October 1961):463-466.

Kornhauser, A. *Mental Health of the Industrial Worker. A Detroit Study.* John Wiley & Sons, Inc., New York, 1965.

Laughlin, H. P. and Hall, M. "Psychiatry for Executives: An Experiment in the Use of Group Analysis to Improve Relationships in an Organization." *American Journal of Psychiatry* 107 (1951): 493-497.

Leavitt, H. J. "Unhuman Organizations." *Harvard Business Review* 40, No. 4 (August 1962):90-98.

Levinson, H. "Alcoholism In Industry." *Menninger Quarterly* 11, No. 2 (1957).

———. *Emotional Health in the World of Work.* Harper & Row, New York, 1964.

———. "Employee Counseling in Industry: Observations of Three Programs." *Bulletin of the Menninger Clinic* 20 (March 1956):2.

Bibliography

——. "The Psychologist in Industry." *Harvard Business Review* 37, No. 5 (1959):93-99.

Levinson, H., Price, C. R., Munden, K. J., Mandl, H. J., and Solley, C. M. *Men, Management and Mental Health.* Harvard University Press, Cambridge, Mass., 1962.

Likert, R. *New Patterns of Management.* McGraw-Hill, New York, 1961.

Ling, T. M. (editor). *Mental Health and Human Relations in Industry.* H. K. Lewis, London, England, 1954; Paul B. Hoeber, Inc., New York, 1955.

MacIver, J. "The Impact of Psychiatry on American Management: A Psychiatrist's View." *Industrial Medicine and Surgery* 31, No. 11 (November 1962):471-476.

Mann, F. C. and Hoffman, L. R. *Automation and the Worker: A Study of Social Change in Power Plants.* Henry Holt & Company, New York, March 1960.

Mann, F. C. and Hoffman, L. R. *Automation and the Worker: A Study tions.* Foundation for Research on Human Behavior, University of Michigan, Ann Arbor, Michigan, 1961.

McGregor, D. M. *The Human Side of Enterprise.* McGraw-Hill, New York, 1960.

McLean, A. A. "Management Discovers Psychiatry." *Think,* p. 6, March 1959.

——. "Occupational Mental Health: Review of an Emerging Art." *The American Journal of Psychiatry* 122, No. 9 (March 1966): 961-975.

McLean, A. A., and Taylor, G. C. *Mental Health in Industry.* McGraw-Hill, New York, 1958.

McLean, A. A., and Wohlking, W. (editors). "The Impact of Psychiatry on American Management." Industrial Medicine and Surgery, 31, No. 11 (November 1962):469-503, and reprint series No. 129. New York State School of Industrial and Labor Relations, Cornell University, Ithaca, N. Y.

McMurray, R. N. "Mental Illness in Industry." *Harvard Business Review* 37 (1959):79-86.

Menninger, W. C. "Prescription for Executive Mental Health." *Advanced Management* 25 (September 1960):16-17.

Menninger, W. C., and Levinson, H. "Human Understanding in Industry: A Guide for Supervisors." Science Research Associates, Chicago, Ill., 1956.

Milt, H. *Basic Handbook on Mental Illness.* Scientific Aids Publications, Fairhaven, New Jersey, 1966.

Mindus, E. "Industrial Psychiatry in Great Britain, the United States, and Canada." A report to the World Health Organization, Geneva, Switzerland, 1952.

Olshansky, S., Grob, S., and Malamud, I. T. "Employers' Attitudes and Practices in the Hiring of Ex-mental Patients." *Mental Hygiene* 42 (1958):391-401.

Perlis, L. "Labor Looks at Mental Health." *Menninger Quarterly,* 9, No. 3 (Summer 1955):21-26.

———. "Labor Viewpoint of Alcoholism in Industry." *Industrial Medicine and Surgery* 27 (October 1958):535-536.

Rennie, T. A. C., Burling, T., and Woodward, L. E. *Vocational Rehabilitation of Psychiatric Patients.* Commonwealth Fund, New York, 1950.

Richardson, F. L. W. and Walker, C. R. *Human Relations in an Expanding Company.* Yale University Press, New Haven, Connecticut, 1949.

Rogers, C. R., and Roethlisberger, F. J. "Barriers and Gateways to Communication." *Harvard Business Review* 30, No. 4 (July-August 1952):46-52.

Rosen, H. "Job Enlargement and Its Implications." *Industrial Medicine and Surgery* 32, No. 6 (June 1963):217.

Ross, W. D. "Mental and Emotional Health Problems in the Worker." *Archives of Environmental Health* 7 (October 1963):473-476.

———. *Practical Psychiatry for Industrial Physicians.* Charles C. Thomas, Springfield, Ill., 1956.

Schulzinger, M. S. *The Accident Syndrome.* Charles C. Thomas, Springfield, Ill., 1956.

Smith, R. A. "The Executive Crack-up." *Fortune,* May 1955.

Solley, C. M., and Munden, K. J. "Behavior of the Mentally Healthy." *Bulletin of the Menninger Clinic* 26 (1962):178-188.

Srole, L., and McLean, A. A. "How to Manage the Psychologically Disturbed Employee." *Business Management* 23 (November 1962):34-39, 56-58.

Srole, L., Langner, T. S., Michael, S. T., Opler, M. K., and Rennie, T. A. C. *Mental Health in the Metropolis: The Midtown Manhattan Study.* McGraw-Hill, New York, 1962.

Stagner, R. *Psychology of Industrial Conflict.* John Wiley & Sons, New York, 1956.

Bibliography

——. "The Psychologist's Function in Union-Management Relations." *Personnel Administration* 26, No. 1 (January-February 1963): 24-29.

Strother, G. B., editor. *Social Science Approaches to Business Behavior.* The Dorsey Press, Homewood, Ill., 1961.

Taylor, G. C. "Work and Leisure in the Age of Automation." *Main Currents in Modern Thought* 22 (May-June 1966):116.

Tredgold, R. F. *Human Relations in Modern Industry.* Butterworth, London, England, 1945. International University Press, New York, 1947, 1950.

Tredgold, R. F. "The Psychiatrist in Industry." *Bulletin of the World Federation of Mental Health* 2, No. 3 (1950):3-7.

Trice, H. M., and Belasco, J. A. "Emotional Health and Employee Responsibility." N.Y.S.S.I.L.R., Cornell University, Bulletin No. 57, May 1966.

Van Alphen de Veer, M. R. *Success and Failure in Industry. A Psycho-medical Study.* Van Gorcum & Comp., Assen., The Netherlands, 1955.

Walker, C. R., and Guest, R. H. *The Man on the Assembly Line.* Harvard University Press, Cambridge, Mass., 1956.

Warshaw, L. J. (editor). "Human Factors and the Work Environment." *Journal of Occupational Medicine* 3 (June 1961):288-301.

Waters, T. C. "Mental Illness: Is it Compensable?" *Archives of Environmental Health* 5 (August 1962):178.

Whyte, W. F. *Money and Motivation.* Harper & Brothers, New York, 1955.

——. *Pattern for Industrial Peace.* Harper & Brothers, New York, 1951.

Zaleznik, A. "The Human Dilemmas of Leadership." *Harvard Business Review* 41, No. 4 (July-August 1963):49-55.

Index

Index

Index

Blood, J. W., 99
Blue Cross, 54
Blue-collar worker stress, 205-206
Brain hemorrhage, 112
Branch, C. H. Hardin, 264
Brecksville Veterans Administration
  Hospital, 237
Brewer, D. L., 264
Brill, N. Q., 116
Burlingame, C. C., 204
Business Management, 5
Business Week, 5
*Butler v. District Parking Manage-
  ment Company*, 117-118

Cadden, Vivian, 149
*Cammeron v. Industrial Commis-
  sion of Arizona*, 109
Caplan, Gerald, 149
Cardiovascular disease, 178, 185
Carter v. General Motors, 114-115,
  117
Center for Occupational Mental
  Health, 247
Chasen, Robert E., 19
Cheney Silk Mills, 204
Childhood dependency, 216-218
Children, mentally ill, 262-263
Children of Working Mothers
  (Herzog), 150
Chrysler Corporation, 209
Churchill, Sir Winston, 160
Cigarette smoking, 181
Clark, Charles, 96
Clinical programs, 61-81
  development, 70-79
    acceptance of, 78
    financial justification, 70-72
    nature of, 72-75
  full-time, 65-66
  goals, 64
  maintaining, 78-79
  meaning of, 63-64
  organizational placement, 75-77
  part-time, 68-70
  staff selection, 77-78, 79-81
Coatsville Veterans Administration
  Hospital, 236
Cole, N. J., 264

Collins, Ralph T., 231-243, 275
Committee on Occupational Psychiatry, 250
Committee on Private Practice in
  Psychiatry, 244
*Community Mental Health Center,
  An Analysis of Existing
  Models* (Glasscote, Sanders,
  Forstenzer, and Foley), 260
Community mental health centers,
  247, 259-269
  aims of, 259-260
  development of, 265-266
  federal grants, 260
  hospitalized patients, 262
  information service, 266-267
  liaison with industry, 265-268
  programs for mentally ill chil-
    dren, 262-263
  rehabilitation programs, 263-265
  securing funds, 262
Community Mental Health Centers
  Act, 34
*Comprehensive Community Mental
  Health Center: Concept and
  Challenge, The*, 260
Compulsiveness, 94-95
Confederation of British Industries,
  170
Confidentiality, 197, 199-200
Conflict
  dependency and, 213-227
    childhood, 216-218
    compensation, 225-226
    labor's attitude, 218
    management's attitude, 218
    supervisors, 224-225
    work environment, 223-224
  labor-management, 195-198, 218
Connecticut Board of Mediation
  and Arbitration, 21
Continental Insurance Company,
  214
Convergence, 89, 92
Conversion hysteria, 110
Cornell University, 5
Council of Social Agencies, 250
Counseling, Occupational Training,
  Placement, and Evaluation

Index